name

PRACTICE

WORKSHEET **1**

Order to 10

a. Write the numbers in order.

0	1	2	3	4	5	6	7	8	9	10
0	1									

b. Write the missing numbers.

2	3	4
4	5	
8	9	

0		2
5		7
3		5

	9	10
	7	8
	2	3

c. Draw a line to match.

1	three	6	seven
2	one	7	ten
3	two	8	six
4	five	9	eight
5	four	10	nine

Use with text pages 3–4.

name

PRACTICE

WORKSHEET **2**

Sums to 6

Complete the addition sentences.

a.

3 + 2 = 5

4 + 1 = ___

1 + 5 = ___

b.

3 + 1 = ___

1 + 2 = ___

0 + 4 = ___

c.

2 + 3 = ___

3 + 0 = ___

1 + 4 = ___

d. 2 + 2 = 4 1 + 2 = ___ 5 + 0 = ___

e. 3 + 1 = ___ 3 + 3 = ___ 2 + 3 = ___

f. 2 + 4 = ___ 0 + 6 = ___ 1 + 4 = ___

g. 5 + 1 = ___ 1 + 1 = ___ 4 + 0 = ___

Use with text pages 5–6.

name

PRACTICE

WORKSHEET **3**

Addition in Any Order

a. 1 + 3 = 4 3 + 1 = 4	0 + 2 = ___ 2 + 0 = ___	2 + 4 = ___ 4 + 2 = ___
b. 0 + 6 = ___ 6 + 0 = ___	1 + 5 = ___ 5 + 1 = ___	0 + 3 = ___ 3 + 0 = ___
c. 2 + 3 = ___ 3 + 2 = ___	1 + 2 = ___ 2 + 1 = ___	1 + 4 = ___ 4 + 1 = ___
d. 1 + 0 = ___ 0 + 1 = ___	4 + 2 = ___ 2 + 4 = ___	0 + 5 = ___ 5 + 0 = ___

Use with text pages 7–8.

name

PRACTICE

WORKSHEET **4**

Vertical Addition

Find the sums.

a.	4 +1 = 5			3 +3	2 +1	4 +0	2 +3
b.	0 +1	1 +5	2 +2	0 +6	3 +1	0 +3	1 +1
c.	1 +3	0 +5	3 +0	1 +2	5 +1	1 +0	2 +4
d.	1 +4	4 +2	6 +0	0 +4	5 +0	3 +2	0 +2
e.	3 +3	6 +0	5 +1	0 +3	1 +4	3 +1	1 +2
f.	1 +5	2 +0	1 +3	2 +4	2 +3	4 +0	4 +1

Use with text pages 9–10.

name

PRACTICE

WORKSHEET **5**

Sums to 8

Find the sums.

a. 4 + 4 = 8   5 + 2 = ___   8 + 0 = ___

b. 7 + 1 = ___   0 + 7 = ___   6 + 1 = ___

c. 6 + 2 = ___   4 + 3 = ___   4 + 2 = ___

d. 3 + 2 = ___   3 + 3 = ___   3 + 5 = ___

e.	2 + 6 = 8	7 + 0	1 + 4	5 + 1	5 + 0	2 + 4	1 + 6
f.	3 + 3	1 + 7	2 + 3	4 + 4	5 + 3	0 + 6	4 + 1
g.	6 + 0	5 + 2	3 + 4	2 + 6	3 + 5	0 + 5	1 + 6
h.	5 + 3	1 + 7	3 + 3	4 + 3	5 + 1	2 + 5	7 + 0

Use with text pages 11–12.

name

PRACTICE

WORKSHEET **6**

Sums to 10

Add.

a.

5 + 4 = 9

4 + 6 = ____

5 + 5 = ____

b. 9 + 1 = ____ 8 + 2 = ____ 0 + 9 = ____

c. 3 + 5 = ____ 7 + 3 = ____ 6 + 3 = ____

d. 1 + 9 = ____ 8 + 1 = ____ 6 + 4 = ____

e.	2	0	2	3	3	4	9
	+8	+8	+7	+6	+7	+5	+0
	10						
f.	1	6	3	1	8	7	1
	+7	+2	+4	+8	+0	+2	+6
g.	3	4	6	9	4	9	4
	+7	+5	+4	+0	+4	+1	+3
h.	2	5	0	4	2	6	2
	+7	+5	+7	+6	+8	+3	+6

Use with text pages 11–12.

name

PRACTICE

WORKSHEET **7**

Problem Solving • Choosing the Addition Sentence

Ring the addition sentence that matches the picture.

a.

$1 + 2 = 3$

$3 + 0 = 3$

b.

$5 + 1 = 6$

$3 + 3 = 6$

c.

$4 + 4 = 8$

$5 + 3 = 8$

d.

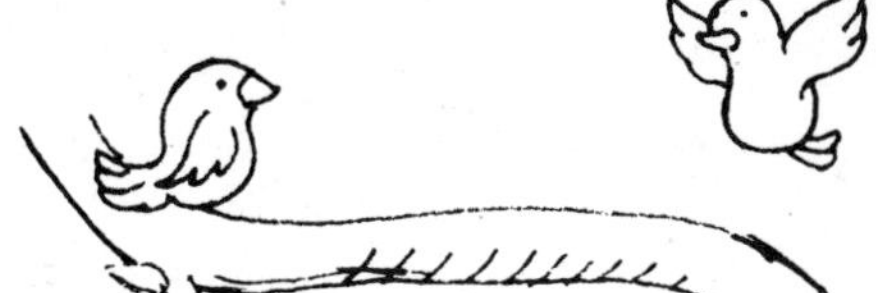

$2 + 0 = 2$

$1 + 1 = 2$

e.

$2 + 3 = 5$

$4 + 1 = 5$

f.

$5 + 4 = 9$

$6 + 3 = 9$

g.

$5 + 2 = 7$

$4 + 3 = 7$

h.

$5 + 5 = 10$

$6 + 4 = 10$

Use with text pages 15–16.

name

PRACTICE

WORKSHEET **8**

Subtraction Sentences

Complete the subtraction sentences.

a.

3 − 2 = 1

b.

2 − ___ = ___

c.

4 − ___ = ___

d.

6 − ___ = ___

Cross out. Then subtract.

e.

4 −   = 2

f.

5 − 3 = ___

g.

6 − 4 = ___

h.

6 − 5 = ___

Use with text pages 19–20.

name

PRACTICE

WORKSHEET **9**

Subtraction Facts to 6 • Related Facts

Subtract.

$6 - 2 =$ 4 $\qquad$ $6 - 4 =$ 2

a. $6 - 1 =$ ___ $\quad 5 - 0 =$ ___ $\quad 4 - 1 =$ ___

$6 - 5 =$ ___ $\quad 5 - 5 =$ ___ $\quad 4 - 3 =$ ___

b. $6 - 0 =$ ___ $\quad 3 - 1 =$ ___ $\quad 2 - 0 =$ ___

$6 - 6 =$ ___ $\quad 3 - 2 =$ ___ $\quad 2 - 2 =$ ___

c. $5 - 1 =$ ___ $\quad 4 - 0 =$ ___ $\quad 5 - 2 =$ ___

$5 - 4 =$ ___ $\quad 4 - 4 =$ ___ $\quad 5 - 3 =$ ___

d. $1 - 0 =$ ___ $\quad 6 - 2 =$ ___ $\quad 3 - 3 =$ ___

$1 - 1 =$ ___ $\quad 6 - 4 =$ ___ $\quad 3 - 0 =$ ___

e. $6 - 3 =$ ___ $\quad 4 - 2 =$ ___ $\quad 2 - 1 =$ ___

f. $4 - 1 =$ ___ $\quad 5 - 3 =$ ___ $\quad 6 - 5 =$ ___

Use with text pages 21–22.

name

PRACTICE

WORKSHEET **10**

Vertical Subtraction

Find the differences.

a.	$\begin{array}{r} 5 \\ -3 \\ \hline 2 \end{array}$ ← difference			$\begin{array}{r} 5 \\ -5 \\ \hline \end{array}$	$\begin{array}{r} 4 \\ -0 \\ \hline \end{array}$	$\begin{array}{r} 6 \\ -1 \\ \hline \end{array}$	$\begin{array}{r} 3 \\ -2 \\ \hline \end{array}$
b.	$\begin{array}{r} 6 \\ -3 \\ \hline \end{array}$	$\begin{array}{r} 5 \\ -1 \\ \hline \end{array}$	$\begin{array}{r} 6 \\ -5 \\ \hline \end{array}$	$\begin{array}{r} 3 \\ -0 \\ \hline \end{array}$	$\begin{array}{r} 4 \\ -3 \\ \hline \end{array}$	$\begin{array}{r} 6 \\ -6 \\ \hline \end{array}$	$\begin{array}{r} 5 \\ -4 \\ \hline \end{array}$
c.	$\begin{array}{r} 6 \\ -4 \\ \hline \end{array}$	$\begin{array}{r} 6 \\ -0 \\ \hline \end{array}$	$\begin{array}{r} 3 \\ -3 \\ \hline \end{array}$	$\begin{array}{r} 5 \\ -2 \\ \hline \end{array}$	$\begin{array}{r} 4 \\ -4 \\ \hline \end{array}$	$\begin{array}{r} 4 \\ -2 \\ \hline \end{array}$	$\begin{array}{r} 2 \\ -1 \\ \hline \end{array}$
d.	$\begin{array}{r} 5 \\ -0 \\ \hline \end{array}$	$\begin{array}{r} 3 \\ -1 \\ \hline \end{array}$	$\begin{array}{r} 2 \\ -0 \\ \hline \end{array}$	$\begin{array}{r} 6 \\ -2 \\ \hline \end{array}$	$\begin{array}{r} 1 \\ -0 \\ \hline \end{array}$	$\begin{array}{r} 4 \\ -1 \\ \hline \end{array}$	$\begin{array}{r} 2 \\ -2 \\ \hline \end{array}$
e.	$\begin{array}{r} 6 \\ -3 \\ \hline \end{array}$	$\begin{array}{r} 4 \\ -2 \\ \hline \end{array}$	$\begin{array}{r} 5 \\ -1 \\ \hline \end{array}$	$\begin{array}{r} 6 \\ -2 \\ \hline \end{array}$	$\begin{array}{r} 6 \\ -5 \\ \hline \end{array}$	$\begin{array}{r} 5 \\ -3 \\ \hline \end{array}$	$\begin{array}{r} 3 \\ -1 \\ \hline \end{array}$
f.	$\begin{array}{r} 4 \\ -4 \\ \hline \end{array}$	$\begin{array}{r} 6 \\ -0 \\ \hline \end{array}$	$\begin{array}{r} 5 \\ -2 \\ \hline \end{array}$	$\begin{array}{r} 5 \\ -5 \\ \hline \end{array}$	$\begin{array}{r} 3 \\ -3 \\ \hline \end{array}$	$\begin{array}{r} 2 \\ -1 \\ \hline \end{array}$	$\begin{array}{r} 6 \\ -6 \\ \hline \end{array}$

name

PRACTICE

WORKSHEET **11**

Subtracting from 7 and 8

Find the differences.

a. $\begin{array}{r} 8 \\ -5 \\ \hline 3 \end{array}$ $\quad$ $\begin{array}{r} 7 \\ -4 \\ \hline \end{array}$

b. $\begin{array}{r} 7 \\ -2 \\ \hline \end{array}$ $\begin{array}{r} 6 \\ -4 \\ \hline \end{array}$ $\begin{array}{r} 8 \\ -0 \\ \hline \end{array}$ $\begin{array}{r} 5 \\ -1 \\ \hline \end{array}$ $\begin{array}{r} 8 \\ -1 \\ \hline \end{array}$ $\begin{array}{r} 7 \\ -5 \\ \hline \end{array}$ $\begin{array}{r} 6 \\ -3 \\ \hline \end{array}$

c. $\begin{array}{r} 8 \\ -4 \\ \hline \end{array}$ $\begin{array}{r} 5 \\ -0 \\ \hline \end{array}$ $\begin{array}{r} 6 \\ -5 \\ \hline \end{array}$ $\begin{array}{r} 7 \\ -3 \\ \hline \end{array}$ $\begin{array}{r} 8 \\ -2 \\ \hline \end{array}$ $\begin{array}{r} 5 \\ -2 \\ \hline \end{array}$ $\begin{array}{r} 6 \\ -0 \\ \hline \end{array}$

d. $\begin{array}{r} 7 \\ -6 \\ \hline \end{array}$ $\begin{array}{r} 6 \\ -2 \\ \hline \end{array}$ $\begin{array}{r} 8 \\ -5 \\ \hline \end{array}$ $\begin{array}{r} 4 \\ -1 \\ \hline \end{array}$ $\begin{array}{r} 3 \\ -2 \\ \hline \end{array}$ $\begin{array}{r} 6 \\ -1 \\ \hline \end{array}$ $\begin{array}{r} 8 \\ -8 \\ \hline \end{array}$

e. $\begin{array}{r} 8 \\ -2 \\ \hline \end{array}$ $\begin{array}{r} 5 \\ -3 \\ \hline \end{array}$ $\begin{array}{r} 8 \\ -3 \\ \hline \end{array}$ $\begin{array}{r} 7 \\ -0 \\ \hline \end{array}$ $\begin{array}{r} 8 \\ -6 \\ \hline \end{array}$ $\begin{array}{r} 7 \\ -2 \\ \hline \end{array}$ $\begin{array}{r} 7 \\ -7 \\ \hline \end{array}$

f. $\begin{array}{r} 7 \\ -4 \\ \hline \end{array}$ $\begin{array}{r} 8 \\ -7 \\ \hline \end{array}$ $\begin{array}{r} 6 \\ -6 \\ \hline \end{array}$ $\begin{array}{r} 5 \\ -4 \\ \hline \end{array}$ $\begin{array}{r} 8 \\ -3 \\ \hline \end{array}$ $\begin{array}{r} 5 \\ -5 \\ \hline \end{array}$ $\begin{array}{r} 7 \\ -1 \\ \hline \end{array}$

name

PRACTICE

WORKSHEET **12**

Subtracting from 9 and 10

Find the differences.

a. ◇ ◇ ◇ ◇ ◇ ◇ ◇̸ ◇̸ ◇̸ ◇̸

$$\begin{array}{r} 10 \\ -\ 4 \\ \hline 6 \end{array}$$

◇ ◇ ◇ ◇̸ ◇̸ ◇̸ ◇̸ ◇̸ ◇̸

$$\begin{array}{r} 9 \\ -6 \\ \hline \end{array}$$

b. $\begin{array}{r} 9 \\ -5 \\ \hline \end{array}$ $\begin{array}{r} 8 \\ -8 \\ \hline \end{array}$ $\begin{array}{r} 9 \\ -1 \\ \hline \end{array}$ $\begin{array}{r} 10 \\ -\ 2 \\ \hline \end{array}$ $\begin{array}{r} 7 \\ -0 \\ \hline \end{array}$ $\begin{array}{r} 9 \\ -7 \\ \hline \end{array}$ $\begin{array}{r} 10 \\ -\ 5 \\ \hline \end{array}$

c. $\begin{array}{r} 10 \\ -\ 1 \\ \hline \end{array}$ $\begin{array}{r} 9 \\ -4 \\ \hline \end{array}$ $\begin{array}{r} 9 \\ -9 \\ \hline \end{array}$ $\begin{array}{r} 10 \\ -\ 6 \\ \hline \end{array}$ $\begin{array}{r} 7 \\ -2 \\ \hline \end{array}$ $\begin{array}{r} 8 \\ -4 \\ \hline \end{array}$ $\begin{array}{r} 9 \\ -2 \\ \hline \end{array}$

d. $\begin{array}{r} 9 \\ -9 \\ \hline \end{array}$ $\begin{array}{r} 10 \\ -\ 7 \\ \hline \end{array}$ $\begin{array}{r} 8 \\ -5 \\ \hline \end{array}$ $\begin{array}{r} 9 \\ -8 \\ \hline \end{array}$ $\begin{array}{r} 10 \\ -\ 2 \\ \hline \end{array}$ $\begin{array}{r} 7 \\ -3 \\ \hline \end{array}$ $\begin{array}{r} 10 \\ -\ 9 \\ \hline \end{array}$

e. $\begin{array}{r} 9 \\ -0 \\ \hline \end{array}$ $\begin{array}{r} 7 \\ -4 \\ \hline \end{array}$ $\begin{array}{r} 10 \\ -\ 3 \\ \hline \end{array}$ $\begin{array}{r} 10 \\ -\ 1 \\ \hline \end{array}$ $\begin{array}{r} 9 \\ -5 \\ \hline \end{array}$ $\begin{array}{r} 9 \\ -1 \\ \hline \end{array}$ $\begin{array}{r} 8 \\ -6 \\ \hline \end{array}$

f. $\begin{array}{r} 9 \\ -3 \\ \hline \end{array}$ $\begin{array}{r} 10 \\ -\ 4 \\ \hline \end{array}$ $\begin{array}{r} 8 \\ -7 \\ \hline \end{array}$ $\begin{array}{r} 9 \\ -6 \\ \hline \end{array}$ $\begin{array}{r} 7 \\ -1 \\ \hline \end{array}$ $\begin{array}{r} 10 \\ -\ 8 \\ \hline \end{array}$ $\begin{array}{r} 10 \\ -\ 7 \\ \hline \end{array}$

name

PRACTICE

WORKSHEET **13 A**

Families of Facts

Add or subtract.

a.

1 + 9 = 10

9 + 1 = ____

10 − 1 = ____

10 − 9 = ____

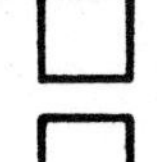

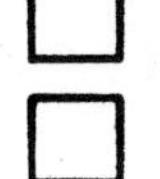

3 + 6 = ____

6 + 3 = ____

9 − 3 = ____

9 − 6 = ____

b.

5 + 3 = ____

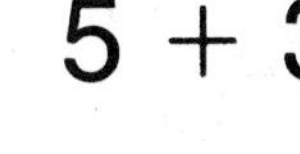

3 + 5 = ____

8 − 5 = ____

8 − 3 = ____

7 + 2 = ____

2 + 7 = ____

9 − 7 = ____

9 − 2 = ____

c.

8	9	5	6	10	2	8
−6	−5	+5	+3	− 3	+7	−4
2						

d.

4	9	7	1	10	6	3
+4	−7	−5	+9	− 5	+2	+7

Use with text pages 29–30.

name

PRACTICE WORKSHEET 13 B

Addition and Subtraction Facts Drill

Add.

a.	2 +8 10	7 +1	0 +9	3 +7	1 +6	4 +6	2 +7
b.	4 +5	5 +5	5 +3	0 +7	6 +4	4 +4	6 +3
c.	8 +0	2 +5	9 +1	6 +2	7 +3	8 +1	3 +4

Subtract.

d.	9 −3 6	10 − 9	8 −3	9 −0	7 −6	10 − 7	8 −1
e.	10 − 6	7 −7	9 −4	8 −4	10 − 5	7 −4	9 −2
f.	7 −5	9 −1	7 −3	10 − 8	8 −2	9 −9	8 −5

Use with text pages 29–30.

name

PRACTICE

WORKSHEET 14

Three Addends

You can add down.	You can add up.
4 } 6 2 +3 ← 9	4 ← 2 } 5 +3 9

Add.

a.

3	3	4	5	3	5	1
2	3	2	1	4	0	4
+5	+2	+4	+3	+2	+3	+2
10						

b.

2	5	3	4	2	3	3
3	2	1	4	2	5	1
+4	+3	+4	+2	+3	+1	+2

The children write letters to their friends each month.
Complete the table. Write how many in all.

	Sue	Keisha	Chris	Ben	Tony
September	4	1	3	2	5
October	3	5	2	4	2
November	3	3	5	2	1
In All	10				

Use with text pages 31–32.

name

PRACTICE

WORKSHEET **15**

Problem Solving • Choosing the Operation

Write + or −.

a.

How many are left?

9 (−) 6 = 3

How many in all?

4 (+) 6 = 10

b.

How many in all?

5 ◯ 4 = 9

How many are left?

8 ◯ 7 = 1

c.	5 ◯ 5 = 10	7 ◯ 4 = 3	9 ◯ 2 = 7
d.	7 ◯ 6 = 1	3 ◯ 5 = 8	6 ◯ 3 = 9
e.	8 ◯ 2 = 10	10 ◯ 1 = 9	2 ◯ 5 = 7
f.	9 ◯ 4 = 5	7 ◯ 1 = 8	8 ◯ 6 = 2
g.	3 ◯ 7 = 10	4 ◯ 4 = 8	10 ◯ 6 = 4
h.	10 ◯ 5 = 5	8 ◯ 3 = 5	4 ◯ 3 = 7

Use with text pages 33–34.

name

PRACTICE

WORKSHEET **16**

Numbers 10 to 19

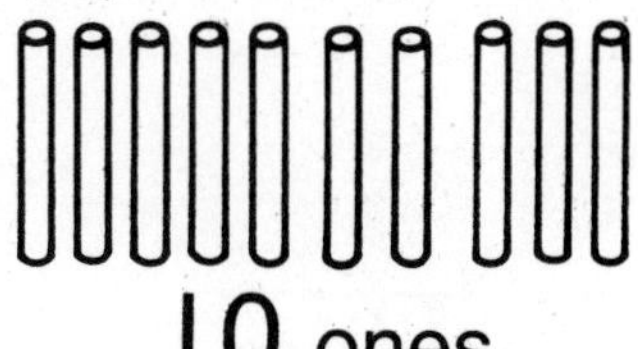

10 ones

make

1 ten.

Write the numbers.

a.

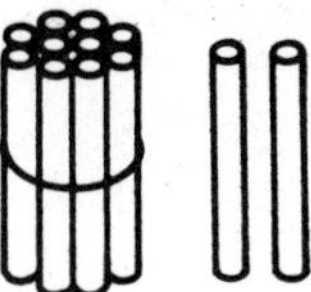

12 ________

b.

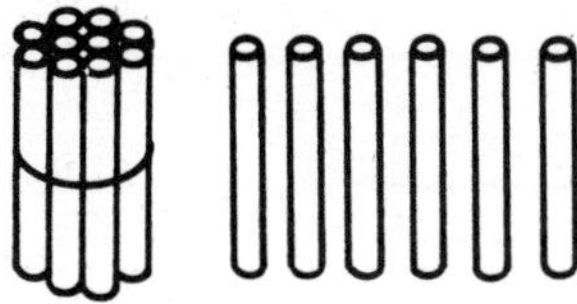

____

c.

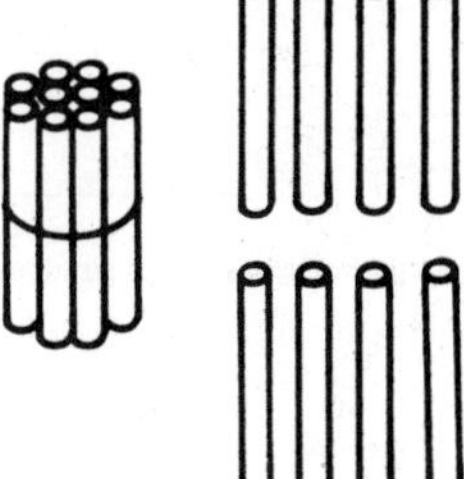

____

d.

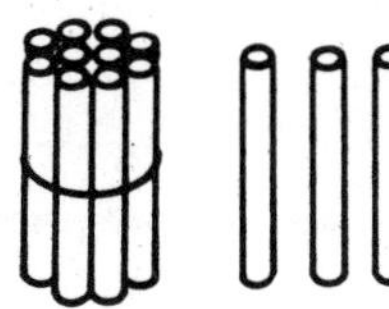

____

Write the numbers.

e.

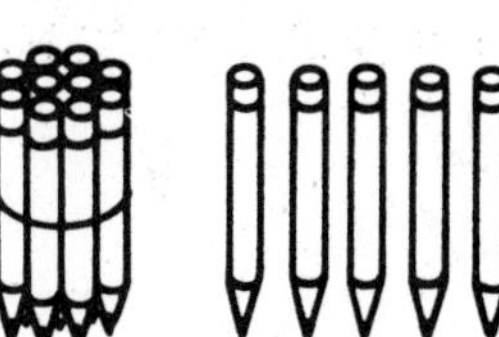

____

f.

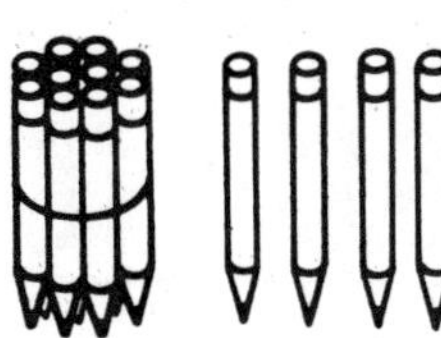

____

g.

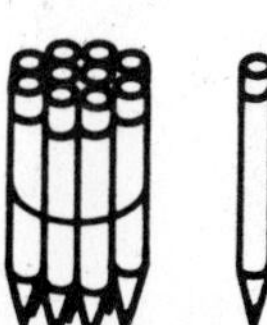

____

h.

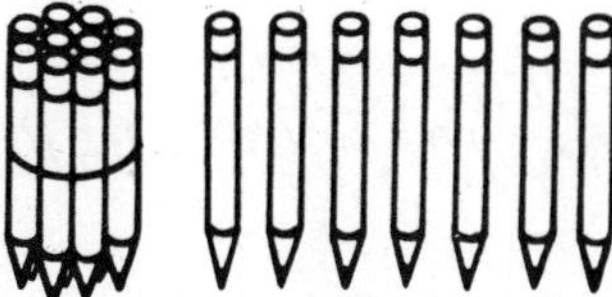

____

name

PRACTICE

WORKSHEET **17**

Tens

Write how many tens.
Write the numbers.

a. 

1 ten

10

b. 

_____ tens

_____

c. 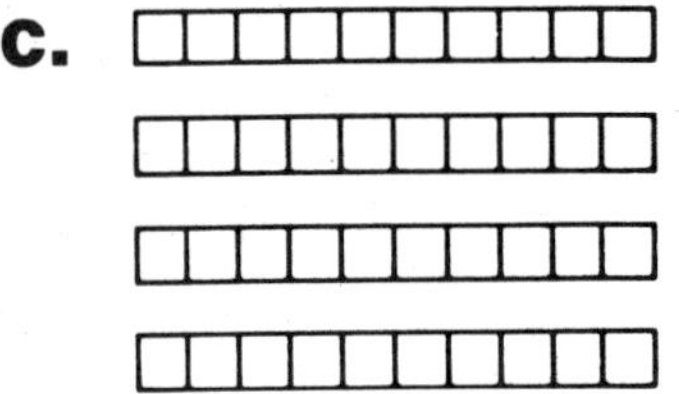

_____ tens

_____

d. 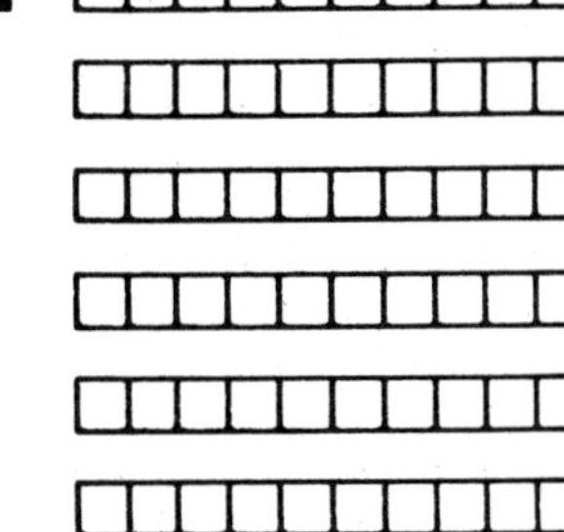

_____ tens

_____

Write the numbers.

e. 

60

f.

_____

g.

_____

h. 

_____

Use with text pages 47–48.

name

PRACTICE

WORKSHEET **18**

Tens and Ones

Write how many tens and ones.
Write the numbers.

a.

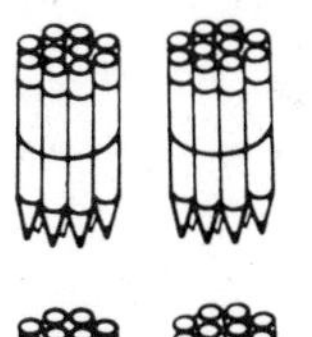

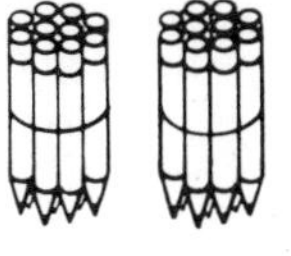

tens	ones
4	2

42

b.

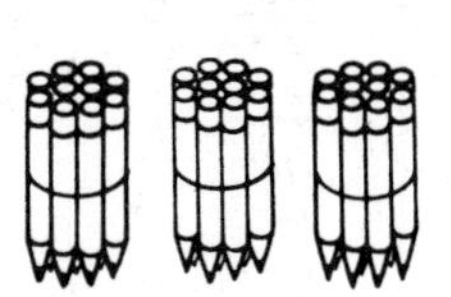

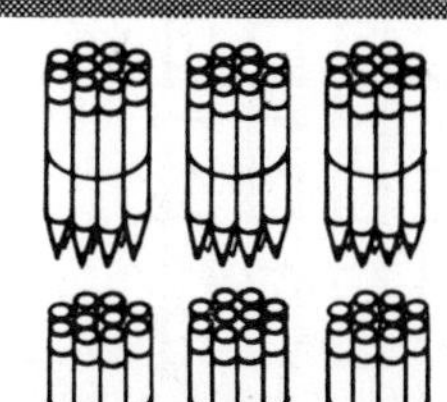

tens	ones

____

c.

tens	ones

____

d.

tens	ones

____

Draw a line to match each picture to the correct number.

e.

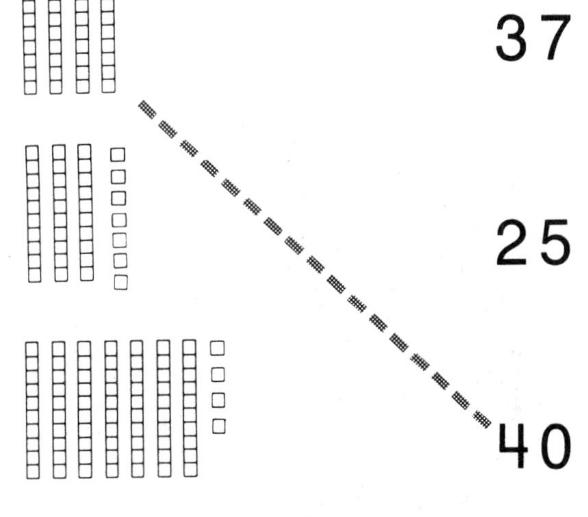

37

25

40

74

f.

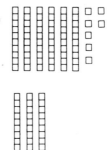

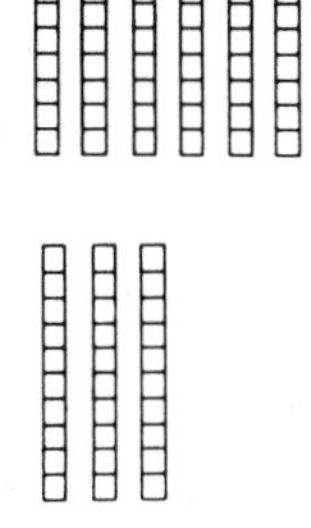

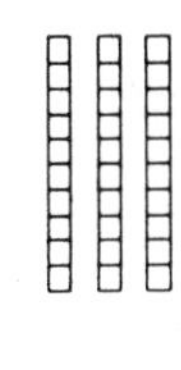

25

67

43

30

Use with text pages 49–50.

name

PRACTICE

WORKSHEET **19**

More about Tens and Ones

Write the numbers.

a. 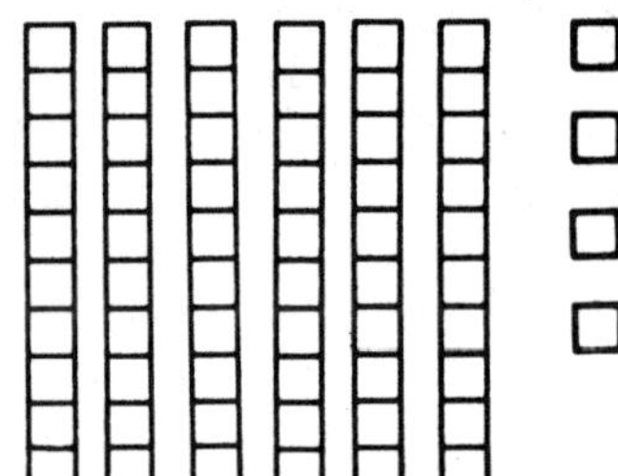  64 | 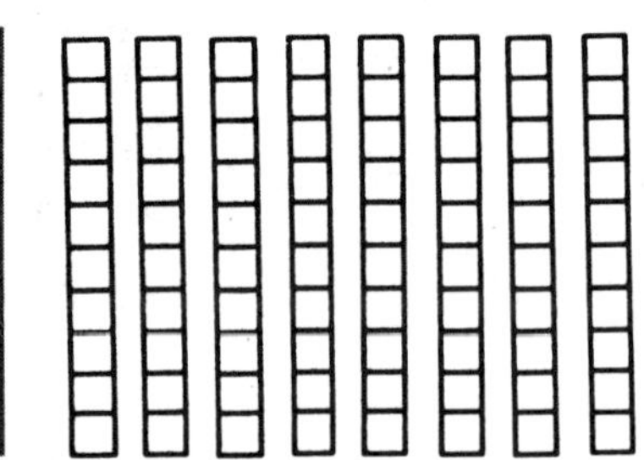 ____

b. 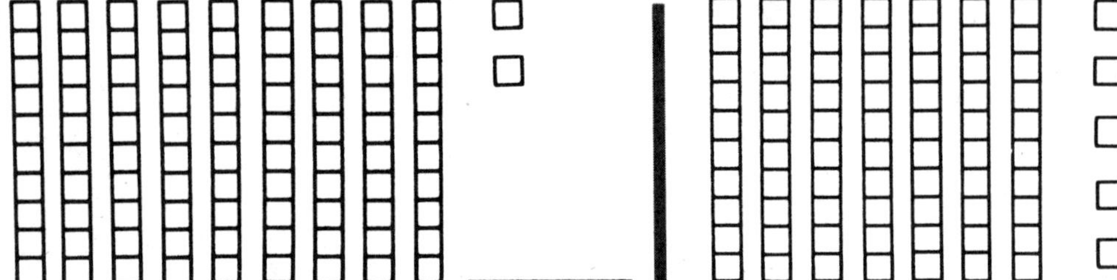 ____ | ____

Complete.

c.	68 = 6 tens 8 ones	83 = ____ tens ____ ones
d.	40 = ____ tens ____ ones	67 = ____ tens ____ ones
e.	15 = ____ tens ____ ones	51 = ____ tens ____ ones
f.	96 = ____ tens ____ ones	26 = ____ tens ____ ones
g.	72 = ____ tens ____ ones	39 = ____ tens ____ ones

name

PRACTICE

WORKSHEET **20**

Order to 100

Write the missing numbers.

a.

b.

c.

d.

e.

f.

Use with text pages 55–56.

name

PRACTICE

WORKSHEET **21**

Counting Patterns

Count by fives.

a. 5, 10, ___, ___, ___,

___, ___, ___, ___, ___,

___, ___, ___, ___, ___,

___, ___, ___, ___, 100

Count by tens.

b. 10, 20, ___, ___, ___,

___, ___, ___, ___, 100

Count by twos.

c.

1	2	3	4	5	6	7		9	
11		13		15		17		19	
21		23		25		27		29	
31		33		35		37		39	
41		43		45		47		49	

name

PRACTICE

WORKSHEET **22**

Greater Than and Less Than

Ring the number that is greater.

a.

76	13	55	18	36	85	20	37
74	15	65	15	46	75	22	34

Ring the number that is less.

b.

45	35	45	37	96	15	26	64
42	33	47	40	92	12	27	54

Write the number that is 1 more.

c.

15	16		24			49	

d.

87			50			36	

Write the number that is 1 less.

e.

42	43			19			35

f.

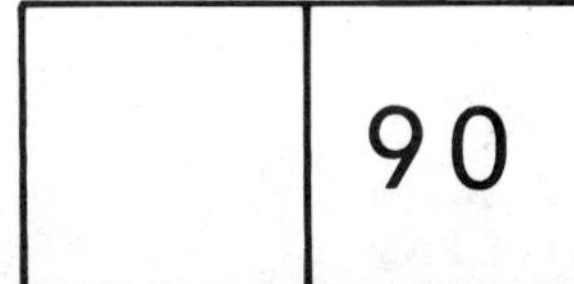

	90			73			51

Use with text pages 59–60.

name

PRACTICE

WORKSHEET **23**

Comparing Numbers

5 is **greater** than 2.	2 is **less** than 5.
5 > 2	2 < 5

Write > or <.

a.

15  18

24  20

b.

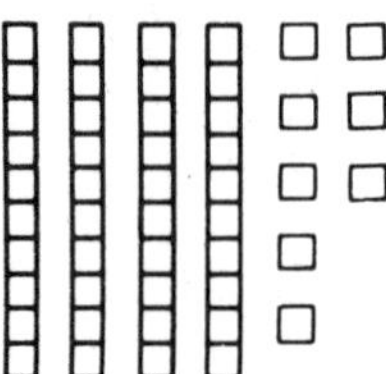 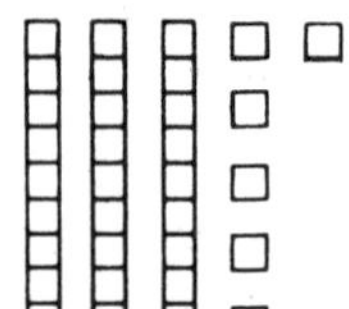

48  36

 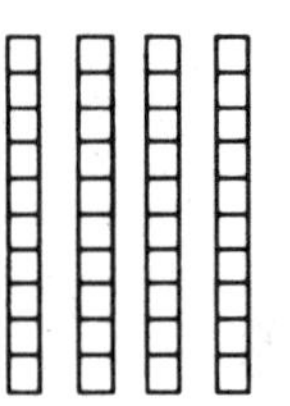 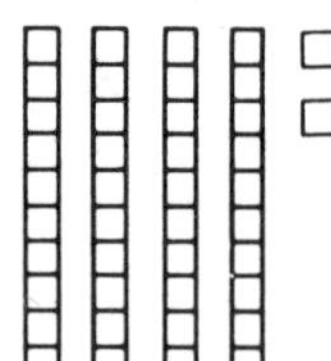

40 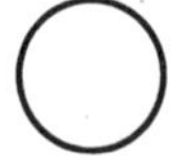 42

c. 54  52   35  45   43  40

d. 60  70   56  54   67  69

e. 85  83   60  64   97  95

f. 76  67   24  28   85  90

Use with text pages 61–62.

name

PRACTICE

WORKSHEET **24**

Ordinals

Ring the correct position for each.

a.	first	second	third	fourth
b.	seventh	eighth	ninth	tenth
c.	sixth	seventh	eighth	ninth
d.	fifth	sixth	seventh	eighth

Color the correct objects.

third sixth ninth

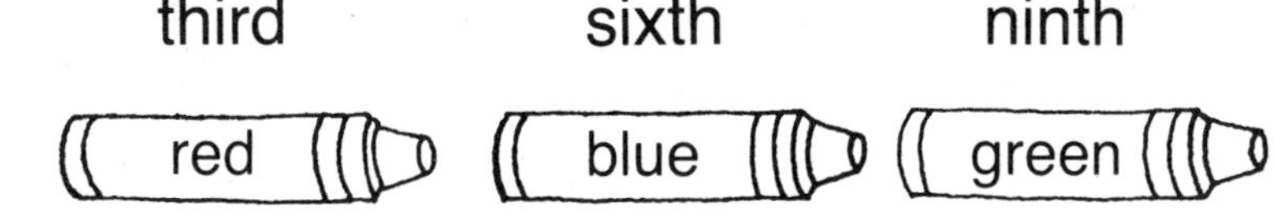

e.

second fifth eighth

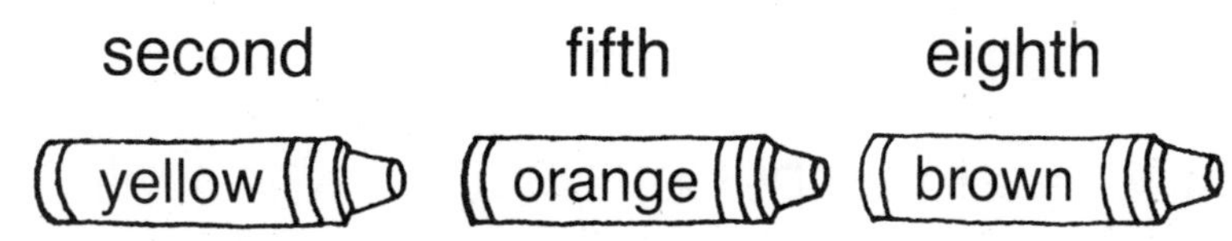

f.

Use with text pages 63–64.

name

PRACTICE

WORKSHEET **25**

Problem Solving • Using a Pictograph

How children come to school	Number of Children
bike	🯅 🯅 🯅 🯅
bus	🯅 🯅 🯅 🯅 🯅 🯅 🯅
walk	🯅 🯅 🯅 🯅 🯅 🯅 🯅 🯅 🯅
car	🯅 🯅 🯅

a. How many children ride a bike? 4

b. How many children ride in a bus? ______

c. How many children walk? ______

d. How many children come by car? ______

e. What is the total number of children who ride a bike or ride in a bus? ______

f. What is the total number of children who walk or come by car? ______

g. How do the fewest number of children come to school? ______

Use with text pages 65–66.

name

PRACTICE

WORKSHEET **26**

Sums to 12

Add.

a. 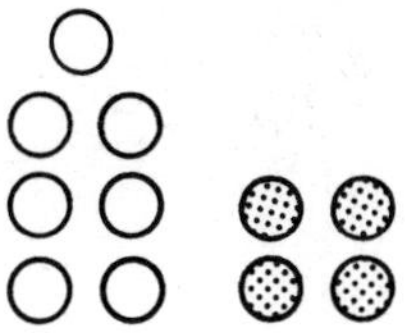 $7 + 4 = 11$ 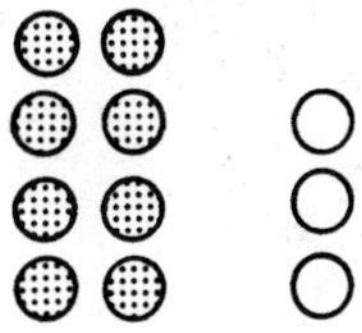 $8 + 3 = \_\_\_$

b. $8 + 4 = \_\_\_$ $9 + 2 = \_\_\_$ $7 + 5 = \_\_\_$

c. $6 + 4 = \_\_\_$ $3 + 8 = \_\_\_$ $6 + 5 = \_\_\_$

d. $9 + 1 = \_\_\_$ $4 + 8 = \_\_\_$ $9 + 3 = \_\_\_$

e. $5 + 6 = 11$ $3 + 9$ $2 + 7$ $1 + 9$ $9 + 2$ $7 + 5$ $3 + 7$

f. $4 + 6$ $2 + 9$ $5 + 5$ $8 + 3$ $0 + 9$ $6 + 5$ $4 + 8$

g. $6 + 6$ $1 + 7$ $4 + 7$ $6 + 3$ $8 + 4$ $8 + 2$ $3 + 8$

h. $5 + 7$ $2 + 9$ $7 + 3$ $3 + 9$ $4 + 4$ $5 + 6$ $3 + 5$

Use with text pages 77–78.

name

PRACTICE

WORKSHEET **27**

Subtracting from 11 and 12

Subtract.

a. □□□□□ □☒☒☒☒☒ 11 − 5 = 6 □□□□□□ ☒☒☒☒☒☒ 12 − 6 = ____

b. 12 − 9 = ____ 11 − 3 = ____ 11 − 9 = ____

c. 10 − 8 = ____ 12 − 7 = ____ 11 − 8 = ____

d. 11 − 7 = ____ 12 − 4 = ____ 12 − 3 = ____

e.

12	10	11	9	8	12	11
− 5	− 2	− 2	− 1	− 2	− 9	− 3
7						

f.

8	11	10	12	9	11	12
− 4	− 4	− 3	− 8	− 3	− 6	− 7

g.

11	10	12	9	11	12	10
− 5	− 6	− 6	− 4	− 9	− 4	− 5

h.

10	12	11	9	12	9	11
− 1	− 3	− 8	− 0	− 5	− 7	− 7

Use with text pages 79–80.

name

PRACTICE

WORKSHEET **28**

Sums to 14

Add.

a. 9 + 4 = 13   8 + 6 = ____

b. 7 + 6 = ____   9 + 3 = ____   8 + 5 = ____

c. 7 + 7 = ____   6 + 7 = ____   8 + 4 = ____

d. 5 + 9 = ____   5 + 8 = ____   6 + 8 = ____

e.

6	3	4	2	5	3	5
+8	+9	+9	+8	+9	+8	+7
14						

f.

2	6	5	4	2	8	3
+9	+7	+6	+8	+7	+5	+7

g.

9	7	7	3	6	8	5
+4	+5	+7	+6	+5	+6	+5

h.

7	9	4	5	5	8	7
+4	+5	+6	+8	+4	+3	+6

name

PRACTICE

WORKSHEET 

Subtracting from 13 and 14

Subtract.

a.	13 − 8 = 5			14 − 7	13 − 9	12 − 6	14 − 8
b.	14 − 5	12 − 3	13 − 6	14 − 6	11 − 9	11 − 7	13 − 4
c.	12 − 5	11 − 8	13 − 5	12 − 9	12 − 4	14 − 9	13 − 7
d.	12 − 7	13 − 8	14 − 5	12 − 8	13 − 9	14 − 6	11 − 5

Add or subtract.

e.	7 + 6 = 13	14 − 8	7 + 7	8 + 5	12 − 6	13 − 5	9 + 5
f.	13 − 4	8 + 6	14 − 9	13 − 6	9 + 4	14 − 7	6 + 7

Go on to Worksheet 29B.

Use with text pages 85–86.

name

PRACTICE

WORKSHEET **29 B**

Subtracting from 13 and 14

Add or subtract.

a.	5	12	14	9	14	13	6
	+8	− 7	− 5	+4	− 8	− 7	+8
	13						

b.	12	5	7	14	7	13	6
	− 4	+9	+6	− 6	+7	− 8	+6

c.	9	13	8	12	9	14	12
	+3	− 9	+5	− 9	+5	− 8	− 8

Problem Solving

Add to solve.

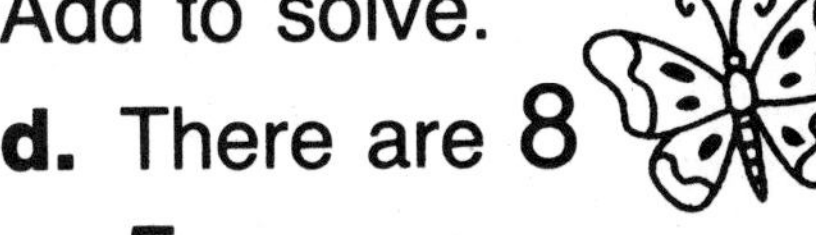

d. There are 8 .
5 more join them.
How many in all?

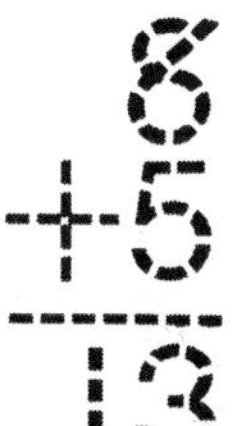

8
+5
13

e. There are 7 .

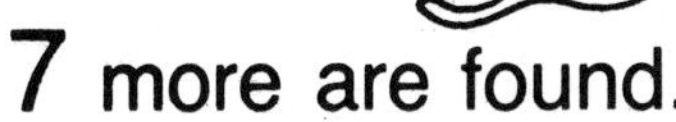

7 more are found.
How many in all?

Subtract to solve.

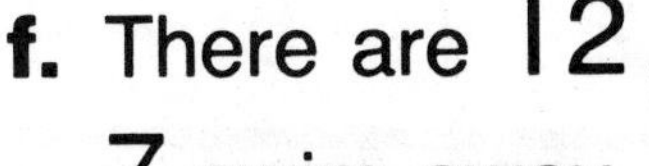

f. There are 12 .
7 swim away.
How many are left?

g. There are 13 .
5 hop away.
How many are left?

name

PRACTICE

WORKSHEET **30 A**

Families of Facts • Names for Numbers

Add or subtract.

a.

4 + 8 = 12	2 + 9 = ___	5 + 9 = ___
8 + 4 = ___	9 + 2 = ___	9 + 5 = ___
12 − 4 = ___	11 − 2 = ___	14 − 5 = ___
12 − 8 = ___	11 − 9 = ___	14 − 9 = ___

b.

5 + 8 = ___	8 + 6 = ___	6 + 7 = ___
8 + 5 = ___	6 + 8 = ___	7 + 6 = ___
13 − 5 = ___	14 − 8 = ___	13 − 6 = ___
13 − 8 = ___	14 − 6 = ___	13 − 7 = ___

Ring each name for the number.

13	(5 + 8)	14 − 5	6 + 7	9 + 4
11	13 − 6	2 + 9	7 + 4	14 − 7
9	14 − 5	13 − 4	6 + 2	5 + 4
7	6 + 5	14 − 7	12 − 5	13 − 6

Go on to Worksheet 30B.

Use with text pages 87–88.

name

PRACTICE

WORKSHEET **30 B**

Addition and Subtraction Practice

Add.
Write the missing numbers.

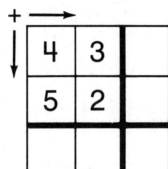

+ →		
6	1	7
3	3	
9		13

+ →		
3	3	
5	0	

+ →		
2	6	
3	3	

+ →		
2	6	
4	0	

+ →		
4	3	
5	2	

+ →		
3	1	
2	7	

Subtract.
Write the missing numbers.

– →		
14	6	8
9	3	
5		2

– →		
13	7	
5	4	

– →		
11	7	
5	3	

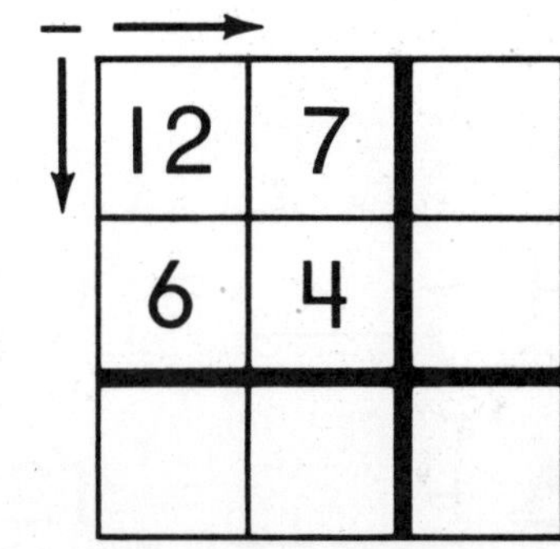

– →		
12	7	
6	4	

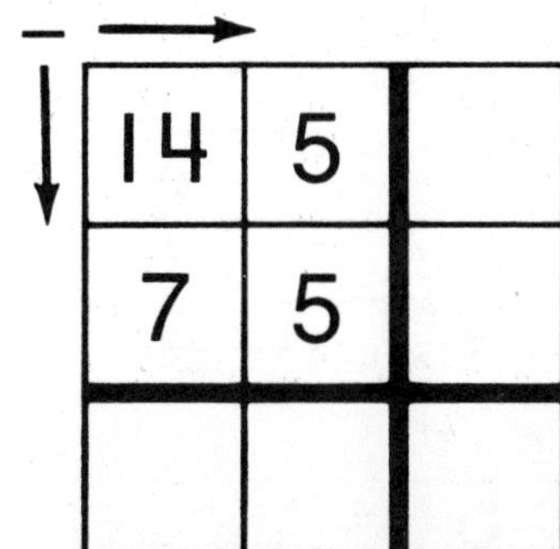

– →		
14	5	
7	5	

– →		
13	6	
4	3	

name

PRACTICE

WORKSHEET **31**

Missing Addends

5 + ____ = 8

5 + 3 = 8

Complete the addition sentences.

a.

6 + 4 = 10

8 + ____ = 10

3 + ____ = 10

8 + ____ = 12

9 + ____ = 12

5 + ____ = 12

b. 6 + 5 = 11   3 + ____ = 12   6 + ____ = 14

c. 2 + ____ = 10   4 + ____ = 11   8 + ____ = 13

d. 9 + ____ = 14   6 + ____ = 13   9 + ____ = 11

e. 8 + ____ = 11   4 + ____ = 12   4 + ____ = 13

f. 7 + ____ = 12   5 + ____ = 11   6 + ____ = 12

Use with text pages 89–90.

name

PRACTICE

WORKSHEET **32**

Problem Solving • Add or Subtract?

post office

stamp

letter

mail truck

mailbox

Ring ADD or SUBTRACT. Then solve.

a. 12 people are at the post office.
9 people leave.
How many people are left?

ADD  SUBTRACT

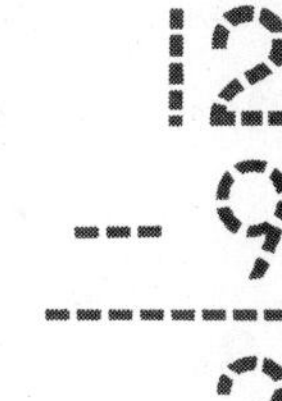

$$\begin{array}{r} 12 \\ -\ 9 \\ \hline 3 \end{array}$$

---

b. Chris buys 7 stamps.
Myra buys 6 stamps.
How many stamps in all?

ADD SUBTRACT

---

c. Chris has 14 letters.
He mails 8.
How many letters are left?

ADD SUBTRACT

name

PRACTICE

WORKSHEET **33**

Sums to 18

Add.

a. 8 + 7 = 15   9 + 8 = ____

b. 9 + 9 = ____   7 + 9 = ____   8 + 8 = ____

c. 6 + 9 = ____   8 + 9 = ____   7 + 8 = ____

d. 7 + 7 = ____   6 + 8 = ____   9 + 6 = ____

e. $\begin{array}{r} 9 \\ +8 \\ \hline 17 \end{array}$ $\begin{array}{r} 8 \\ +7 \\ \hline \end{array}$ $\begin{array}{r} 8 \\ +8 \\ \hline \end{array}$ $\begin{array}{r} 9 \\ +5 \\ \hline \end{array}$ $\begin{array}{r} 8 \\ +9 \\ \hline \end{array}$ $\begin{array}{r} 9 \\ +9 \\ \hline \end{array}$ $\begin{array}{r} 7 \\ +9 \\ \hline \end{array}$

f. $\begin{array}{r} 8 \\ +7 \\ \hline \end{array}$ $\begin{array}{r} 9 \\ +9 \\ \hline \end{array}$ $\begin{array}{r} 8 \\ +6 \\ \hline \end{array}$ $\begin{array}{r} 9 \\ +7 \\ \hline \end{array}$ $\begin{array}{r} 9 \\ +6 \\ \hline \end{array}$ $\begin{array}{r} 8 \\ +5 \\ \hline \end{array}$ $\begin{array}{r} 5 \\ +9 \\ \hline \end{array}$

Problem Solving

Solve.

g. 9 birds are in the tree. 9 more join them. How many birds in all?

h. 7 turtles are in the water. 8 turtles are on the beach. How many turtles in all?

name

PRACTICE

WORKSHEET **34**

Subtracting from 15 to 18

Subtract.

a.

16 − 9 = 7

17 − 9 = ___

b. 18 − 9 = ___ 16 − 8 = ___ 15 − 6 = ___

c. 14 − 6 = ___ 15 − 9 = ___ 16 − 7 = ___

d. 17 − 8 = ___ 14 − 9 = ___ 15 − 7 = ___

e.

14	13	16	15	14	16	15
− 8	− 7	− 8	− 8	− 7	− 9	− 9
6						

f.

13	14	18	17	13	16	17
− 9	− 5	− 9	− 9	− 6	− 7	− 8

Problem Solving

Solve.

g. 15 peanuts in a bag.
6 are eaten.
How many
peanuts are left?

h. 16 apples in a basket.
8 are taken.
How many
apples are left?

name

PRACTICE

WORKSHEET **35**

Families of Facts

Add or subtract.

a.

6 + 9 = 15	5 + 9 = ___	7 + 8 = ___
9 + 6 = ___	9 + 5 = ___	8 + 7 = ___
15 − 6 = ___	14 − 5 = ___	15 − 7 = ___
15 − 9 = ___	14 − 9 = ___	15 − 8 = ___

b.

5 + 8 = ___	7 + 9 = ___	8 + 9 = ___
8 + 5 = ___	9 + 7 = ___	9 + 8 = ___
13 − 5 = ___	16 − 7 = ___	17 − 8 = ___
13 − 8 = ___	16 − 9 = ___	17 − 9 = ___

Write four number sentences.

c.  

Use 6, 8, 14

6 + 8 = 14   ___ − ___ = ___

___ + ___ = ___   ___ − ___ = ___

name

PRACTICE

WORKSHEET **36**

Problem Solving • Two Uses of Subtraction

Draw lines to match. Subtract to compare.	Subtract to find how many are left.
How many more flowers than bees?	There are 15 kites. 8 fly away. How many kites are left?
5 − 3 = 2	15 − 8 = 7

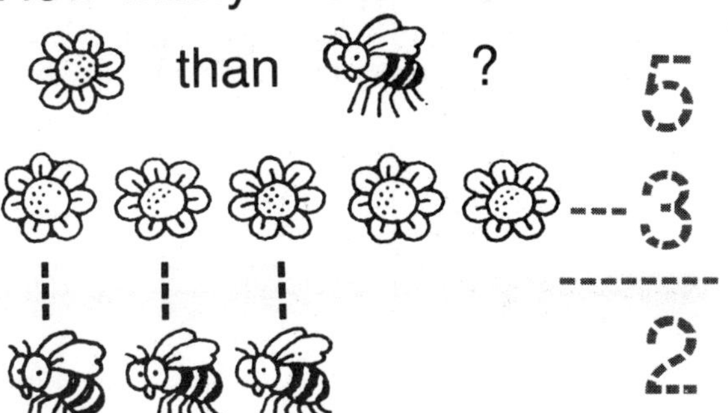

Solve.

a. How many more oars than boats?

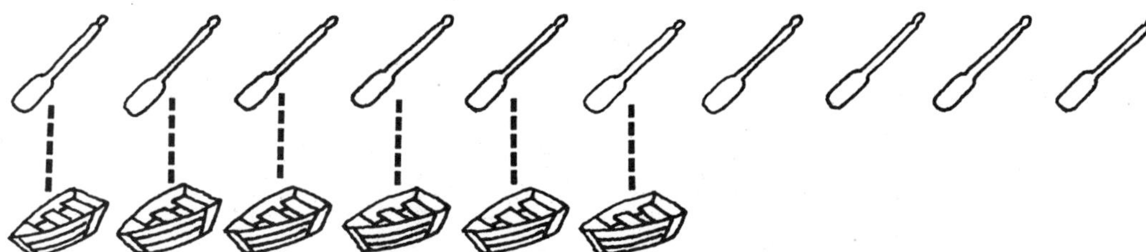

b. You see 11 ducks. You see 6 swans. How many more ducks than swans?

c. There are 15 sailboats. 6 sail away. How many sailboats are left?

d. 16 cars are in a race. 7 stop racing. How many cars are left racing?

e. You count 14 bicycles. You count 6 wagons. How many more bicycles than wagons?

name

PRACTICE WORKSHEET

The Addition Table

Complete the addition table.

+	0	1	2	3	4	5	6	7	8	9
0	0									
1										
2										
3										
4										
5										
6										
7										
8										
9										

Go on to Worksheet 37B.

Use with text pages 113–114.

name

PRACTICE

WORKSHEET **37 B**

Addition and Subtraction Facts Drill

Add.

a.	8	8	7	9	7	9	6
	+9	+7	+9	+9	+7	+6	+8
	17						

b.	6	8	5	8	9	7	9
	+9	+8	+9	+6	+8	+8	+7

Subtract.

c.	17	15	14	18	15	16	14
	− 8	− 6	− 7	− 9	− 8	− 7	− 6
	9						

d.	16	15	14	16	14	15	17
	− 8	− 9	− 5	− 9	− 8	− 7	− 9

Find the above sums and differences in the picture.

Color all sums 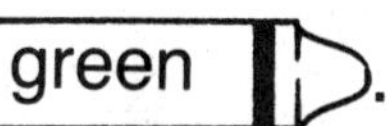

.

Color all differences 

.

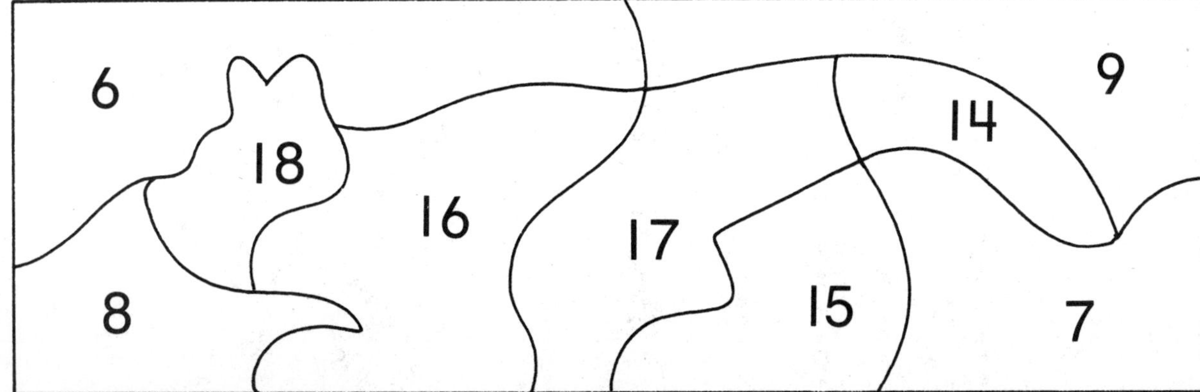

Use with text pages 113–114.

name

PRACTICE

WORKSHEET **38** A

Names for Numbers • Three Addends

Ring each name for the number.

a.

(16)	(8)	(13)	(7)
9 + 7	17 − 9	7 + 5	16 − 9
18 − 9	15 − 7	9 + 4	14 − 7
8 + 8	14 − 8	6 + 7	12 − 5

b.

(9)	(15)	(10)	(6)
18 − 9	17 − 8	2 + 8	12 − 6
5 + 4	8 + 7	5 + 5	13 − 7
7 + 3	9 + 6	4 + 6	15 − 8

Add.

c.

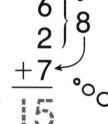

Add the first two numbers.

Then add the third number.

6	5	6	8	4
2 } 8	2	3	1	5
+7	+7	+8	+6	+9
15				

d.

6	8	7	2	4	3	7
2	1	2	6	4	4	1
+6	+7	+4	+8	+7	+6	+4

Go on to Worksheet 38B.

name

PRACTICE

WORKSHEET 38 B

Three Addends

Add.

a.

5	6	8	6	3	7	7
1	1	1	3	2	2	2
+7	+5	+8	+6	+6	+5	+7
13						

b.

3	7	5	4	2	4	5
5	1	2	4	5	2	2
+6	+7	+6	+8	+8	+6	+4

Add.
Match your answers with the letters in the code.
Find the secret message.

14	17	11	15	18	10	12	16	13
A	F	H	I	M	N	S	T	U

3 6 +9	7 1 +6	5 3 +8	2 4 +5
18			
M			

6 2 +7	4 4 +4

7 2 +8	3 4 +6	5 2 +3

name

PRACTICE

Problem Solving • Choosing the Operation

Ring the correct example for each question.
Then solve.

a. The toy store has 8 red bikes.
It has 7 blue bikes.
How many bikes in all?

$$\begin{array}{r} 8 \\ +7 \\ \hline 15 \end{array} \qquad \begin{array}{r} 8 \\ -7 \\ \hline \end{array}$$

b. There are 9 puppets.
There are 6 dolls.
How many more puppets than dolls?

$$\begin{array}{r} 9 \\ +6 \\ \hline \end{array} \qquad \begin{array}{r} 9 \\ -6 \\ \hline \end{array}$$

c. There are 8 games.
You buy 2.
How many games are left?

$$\begin{array}{r} 8 \\ +2 \\ \hline \end{array} \qquad \begin{array}{r} 8 \\ -2 \\ \hline \end{array}$$

Solve.

d. You count 9 books. You count 8 more books. How many books in all?

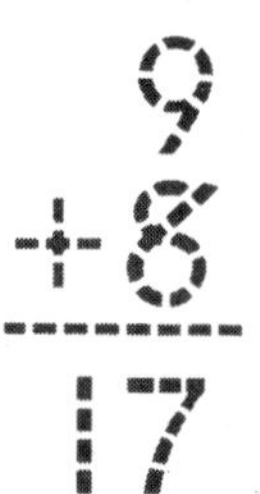

e. There are 14 toy bears. There are 8 toy tigers. How many more bears than tigers?

f. The toy store has 16 toy cars. It sells 7. How many toy cars are left?

g. There are 6 large dollhouses. There are 7 small dollhouses. How many dollhouses in all?

name

PRACTICE

WORKSHEET **40**

Hundreds

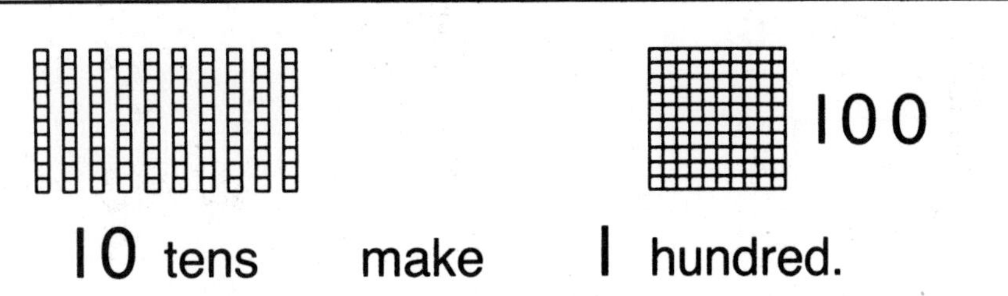

10 tens make 1 hundred.

Count the hundreds. Write how many.

a. 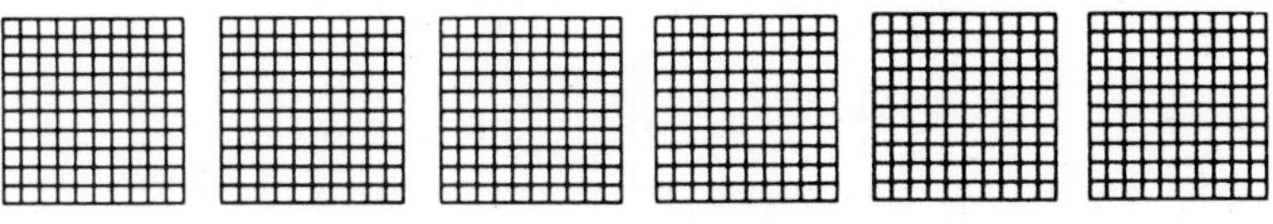

6 hundreds

600

b. 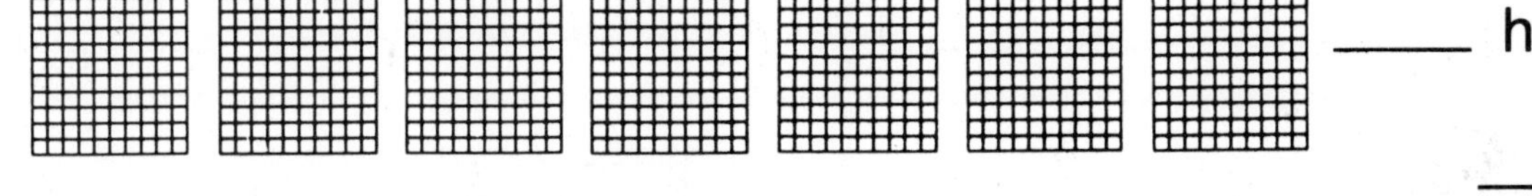

_____ hundreds

____

c. 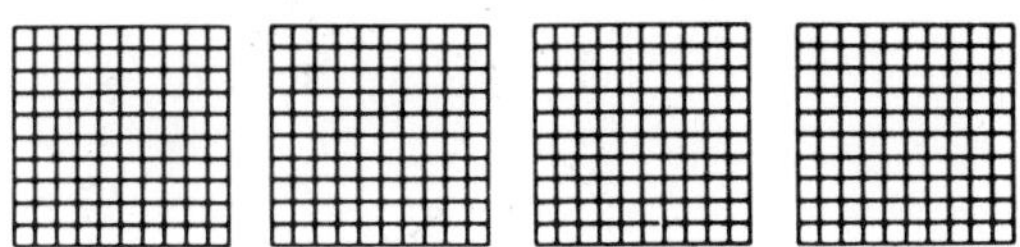

_____ hundreds

____

Write the numbers.

d. 8 hundreds = 800   2 hundreds = _______

e. 4 hundreds = _______   5 hundreds = _______

Problem Solving

Ring the best guess for each problem.

f. There are

5, 50, 500

pencils in your desk.

g. A math class is

5, 50, 500

minutes long.

name

PRACTICE

WORKSHEET **41**

Hundreds, Tens, and Ones

Write the numbers.

a. 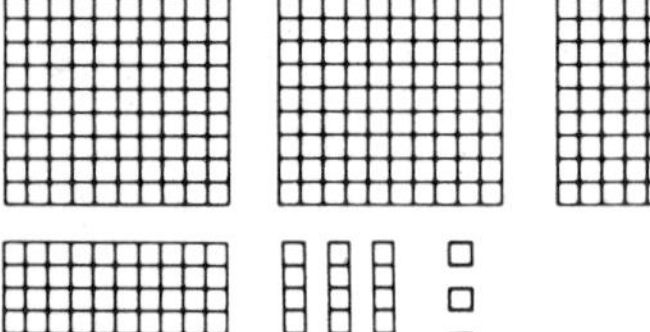

435

b. 

______

c. 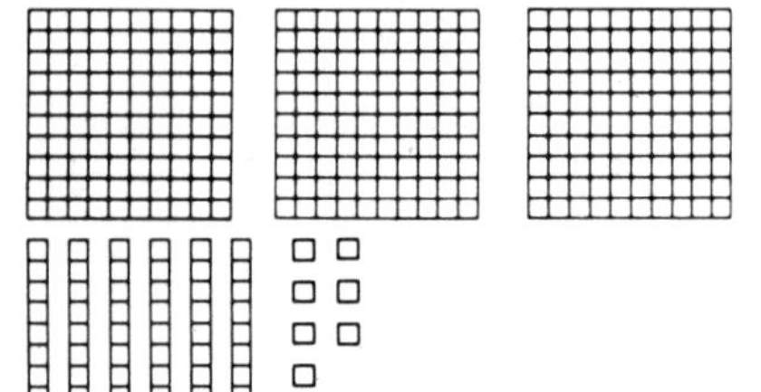

______

d. 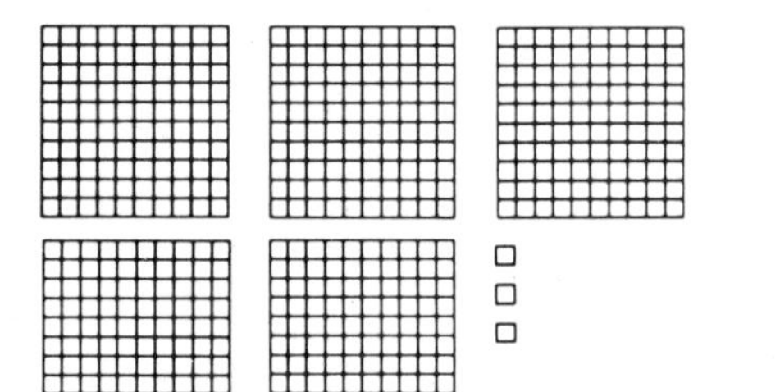

______

e. 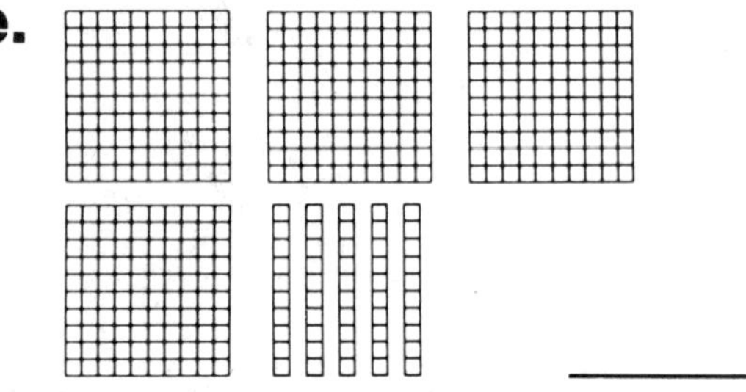

______

f. 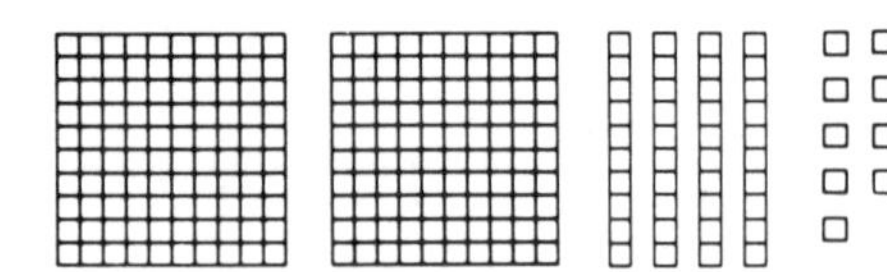

______

g. 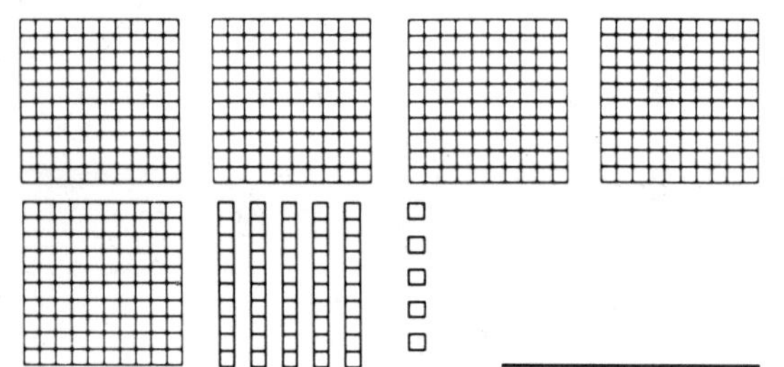

______

h. 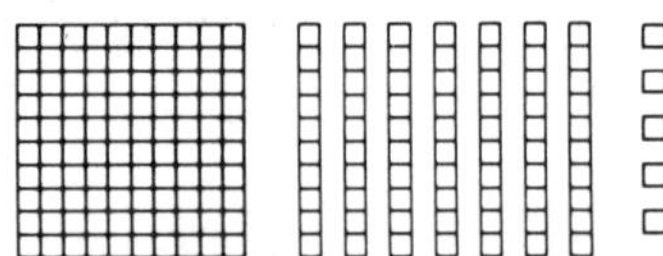

______

Problem Solving

i. This number has a 6 in the hundreds place, a 3 in the tens place, and a 1 in the ones place. What's the number? ______

j. This number has an 8 in the hundreds place, a 5 in the tens place, and a 0 in the ones place. What's the number? ______

Use with text pages 135–136.

name

PRACTICE

WORKSHEET **42**

More About Hundreds, Tens, and Ones

Write the numbers.

a. 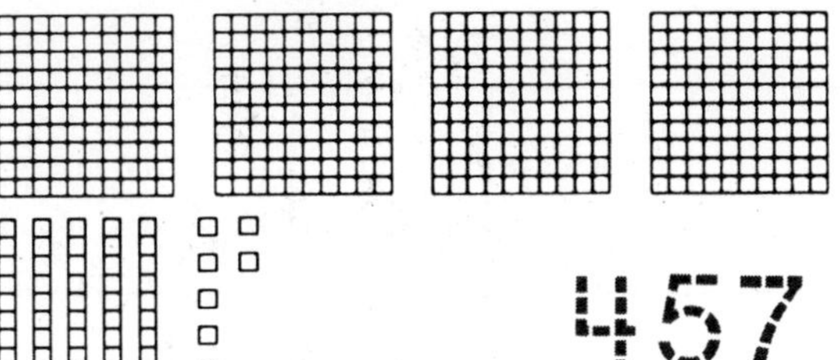 457

b. 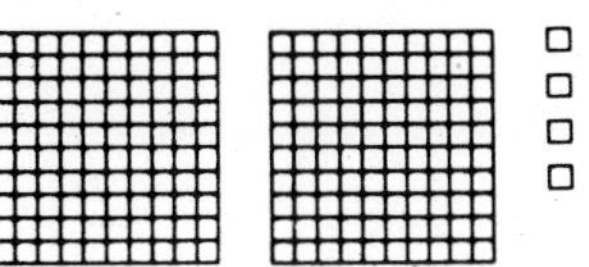 ______

c. 5 hundreds	3 tens	0 ones		530
d. 6 hundreds	0 tens	0 ones		______
e. 4 hundreds	5 tens	7 ones		______
f. 2 hundreds	0 tens	6 ones		______
g. 8 hundreds	9 tens	3 ones		______

Complete.

h. 145	1 hundred	4 tens	5 ones
i. 900	______ hundreds	______ tens	______ ones
j. 864	______ hundreds	______ tens	______ ones
k. 708	______ hundreds	______ tens	______ ones
l. 392	______ hundreds	______ tens	______ ones

Use with text pages 137–138.

name

PRACTICE

WORKSHEET **43**

Order to 1,000

Complete the chart.

a.

201	202	203				207			210
211							218		
	222							229	
				235					240
							248		250

Write the missing numbers.

b.

341	342	343					348		

c.

671				675				679	

d.

801							808		

e.

	532			535					540

name

PRACTICE

WORKSHEET **44**

Counting Patterns

Count by fives.

a.

5	10	15			30				50
		65						95	

b. 105 110 115 ____ ____ ____ 135

c. 340 345 ____ ____ ____ 365 ____

Count by tens.

d.

10	20	30			60				

e. 250 260 ____ ____ ____ 300 ____

f. 580 ____ 600 ____ ____ ____ ____

Count by 50s.
Color the 100s.

g.

50	100	150		250
	350			500
			700	
				1000

Use with text pages 141–142.

name

PRACTICE

WORKSHEET **45**

Greater Than and Less Than

Ring the number that is greater.

a.

386	963	580	804	721	548	720
370	762	697	904	722	538	620

Ring the number that is less.

b.

736	195	920	700	286	483	753
725	205	919	800	285	473	754

Write the number that is 1 more.

c. | 135 | 136 | | 400 | | | 750 | |

d. | 624 | | | 387 | | | 269 | |

Write the number that is 1 less.

e. 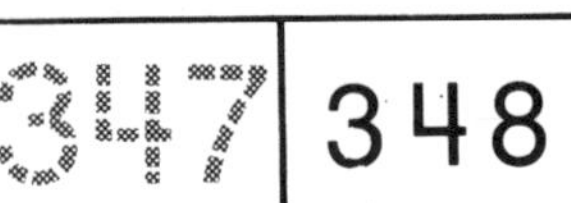 | 348 | | | 607 | | | 184 |

f. | | 725 | | | 230 | | | 876 |

name

PRACTICE

WORKSHEET **46**

Comparing Numbers

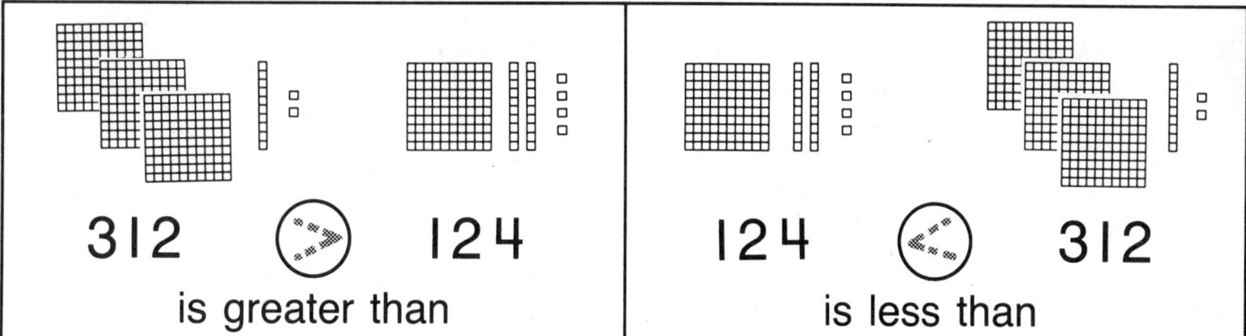

312 > 124
is greater than

124 < 312
is less than

Write the numbers.
Write > or <.

a.

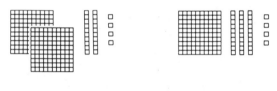

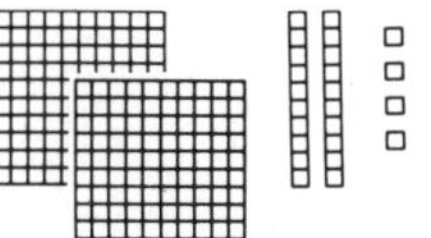

224 > 134

b.

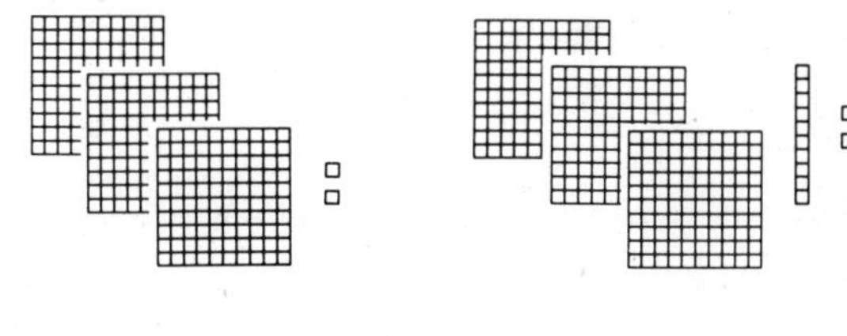

_____ ○ _____

c.

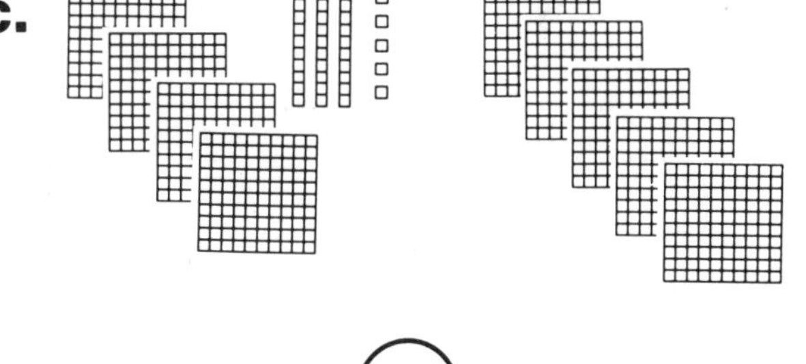

_____ ○ _____

d.

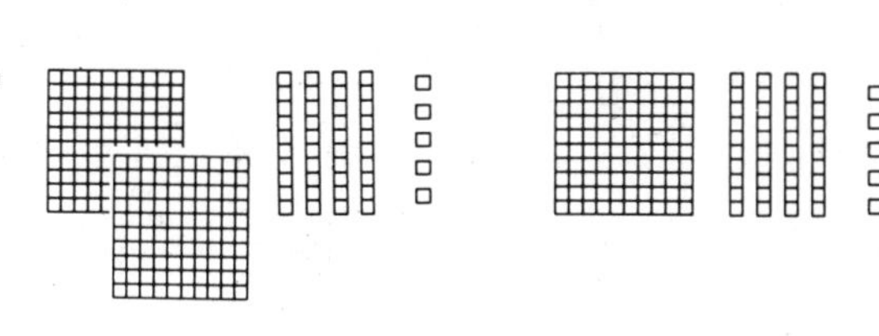

_____ ○ _____

Write > or <.

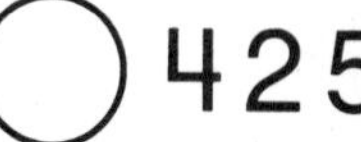

e. 456 < 625   561 ○ 432   408 ○ 425

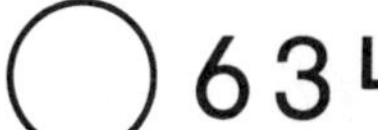

f. 300 ○ 150   743 ○ 723   812 ○ 634

g. 643 ○ 700   639 ○ 640   115 ○ 90

Use with text pages 145–146.

name

PRACTICE

WORKSHEET **47**

Problem Solving • Using Bar Graphs

The children counted the things in the school store and made a graph.

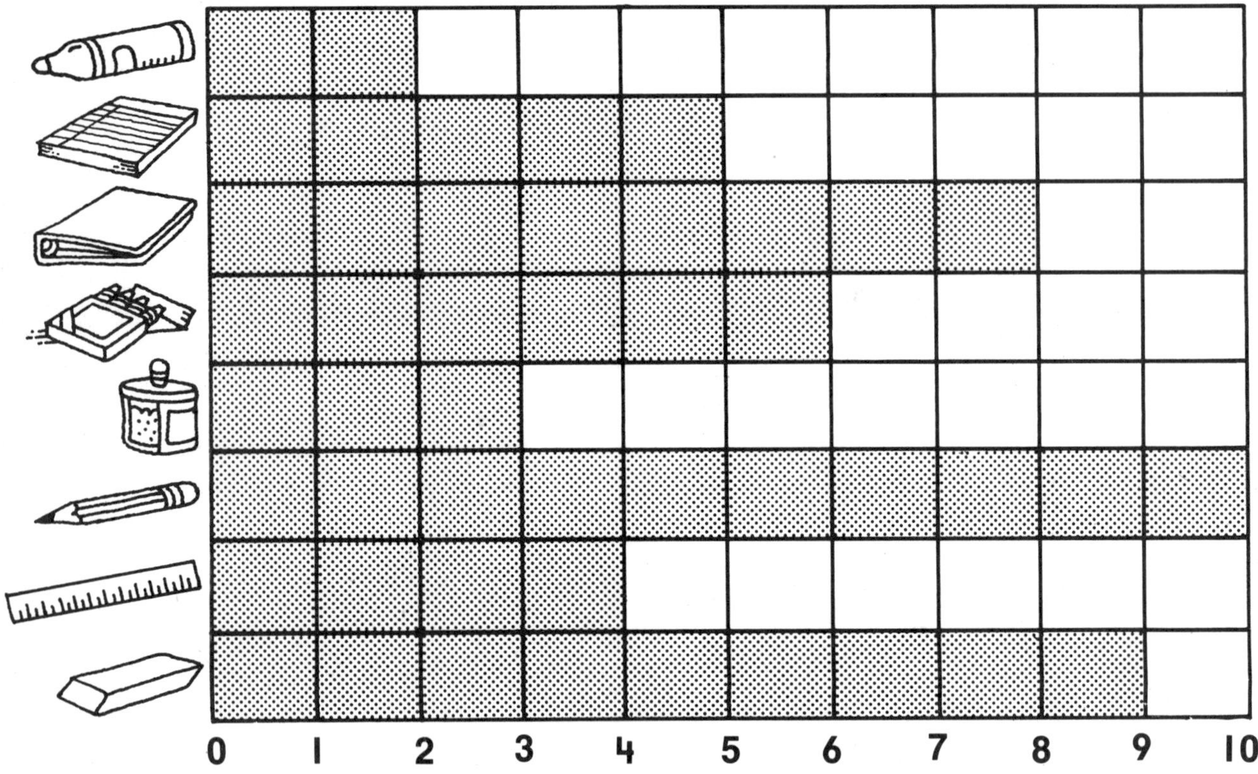

Write how many of each.
Ring the number that is greater.

name

PRACTICE

WORKSHEET **48**

Hour and Half Hour

One hour is 60 minutes.

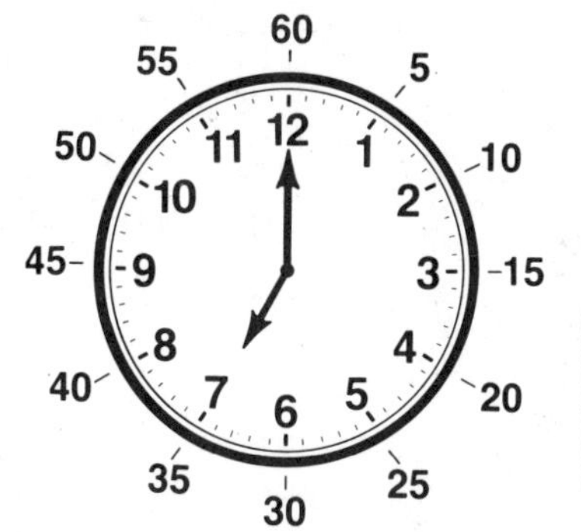

One half hour is 30 minutes.

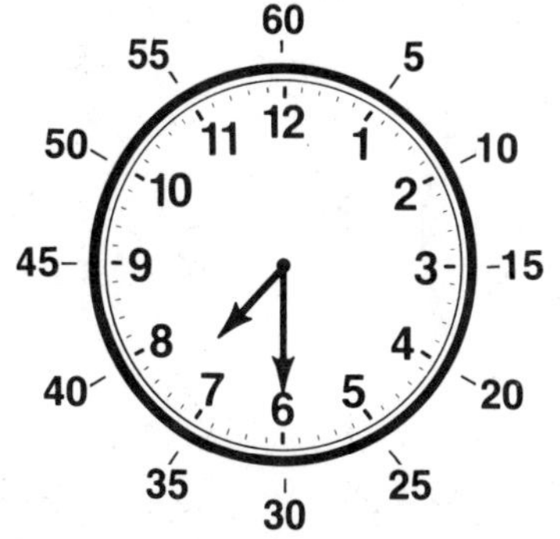

half past 7
seven-thirty

7:30

What time is it?

a.

10:30 __________

____

____

b.

____

____

____

c.

____

____

____

name

PRACTICE

WORKSHEET **49**

Fifteen-Minute Intervals

One quarter hour is 15 minutes.

quarter after 10

quarter to 11

Ring the correct time.

a.

4:00

4:45

b.

7:00

7:15

7:30

c.

3:45

3:15

4:00

d.

2:15

2:30

2:45

e.

12:15

12:00

12:30

f.

4:00

5:00

6:00

name

PRACTICE

WORKSHEET **50**

Five-Minute Intervals

What time is it?

a.

4:05 ______

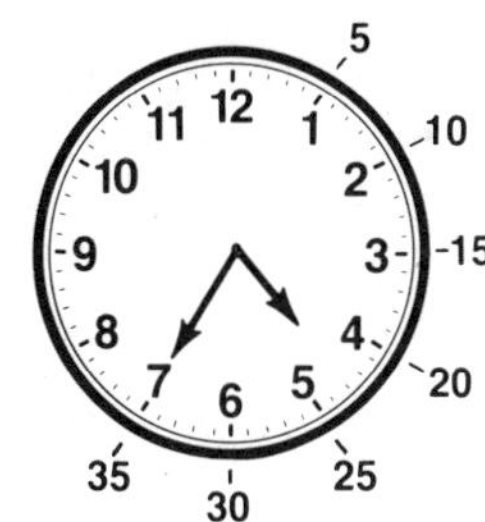

______

______

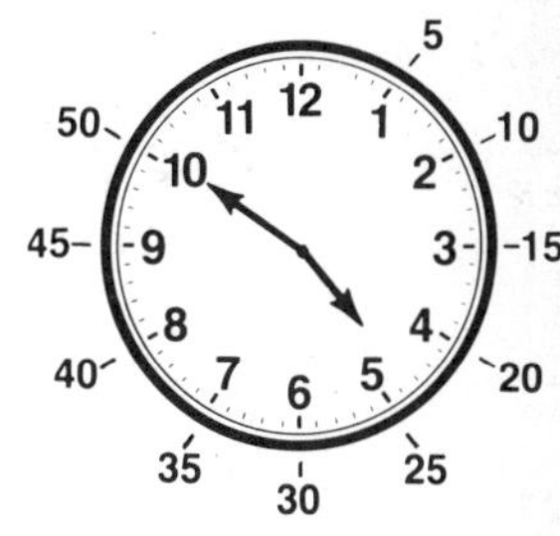

______

b.

______

______

______

______

Draw lines to match.

c.

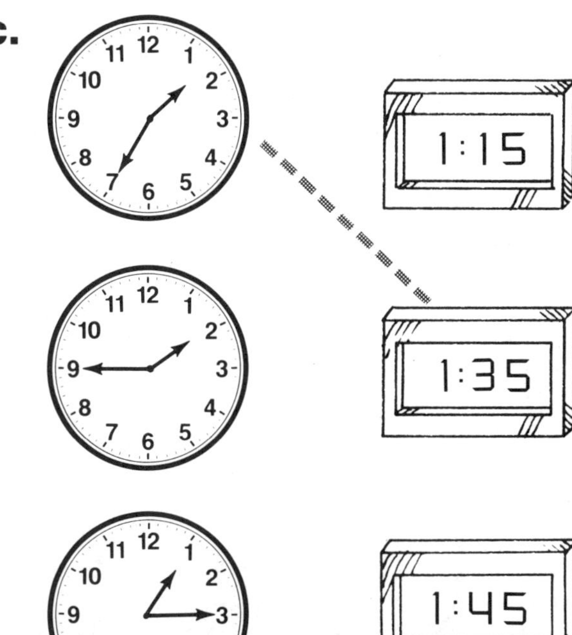

d.

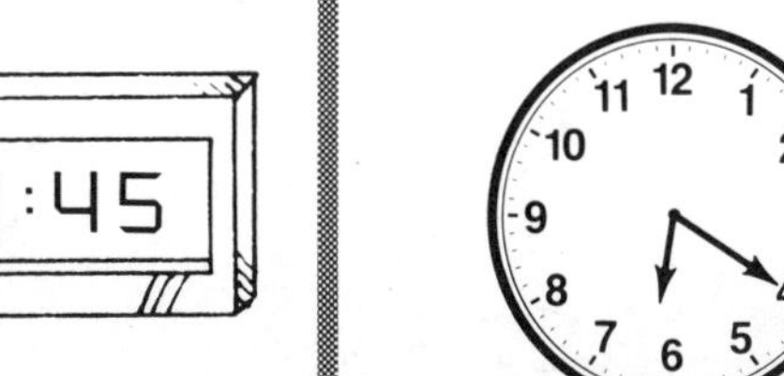

Use with text pages 163–164.

name

PRACTICE

WORKSHEET **51**

Practice in Telling Time

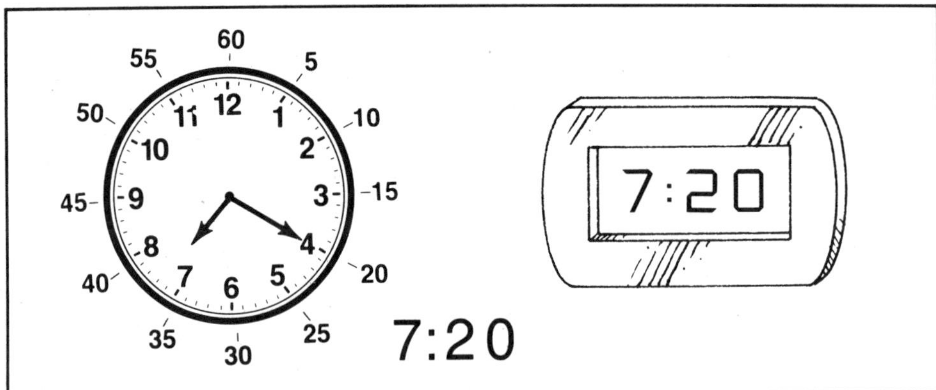

Ring the correct time.

a.

8:10

8:25

8:50

b.

11:30

11:45

11:50

c.

8:35

8:40

8:45

d.

9:05

9:15

9:35

e.

10:10

10:15

10:25

f.

12:20

12:30

12:45

Use with text pages 165–166.

name

PRACTICE

WORKSHEET **52**

The Calendar

Complete a calendar for this month.
Draw a picture to show the weather for each day.

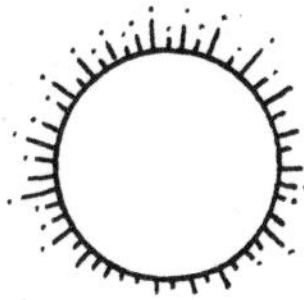

Sunny

Cloudy

Partly Cloudy

Rainy

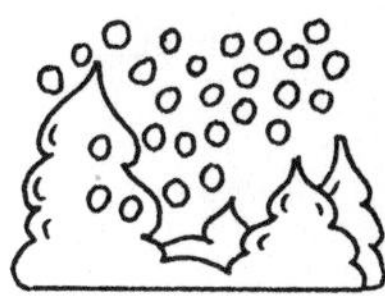

Snowy

Sunday	Monday	Tuesday	Wednesday	Thursday	Friday	Saturday

a. How many sunny days in the first and second weeks? ________

b. How many rainy days in the second and third weeks? ________

c. How many cloudy days in the third and fourth weeks? ________

d. How many partly cloudy days in the month? ________

Use with text pages 167–168.

name

PRACTICE

WORKSHEET **53**

Penny, Nickel, and Dime

penny	nickel	dime

1¢ 1 cent	5¢ 5 cents	10¢ 10 cents

How much money?

a.

17 ¢

_______ ¢

b.

_______ ¢

_______ ¢

Ring how much money is needed.

c.

name

PRACTICE

Quarter

quarter

25¢ 25¢ 25¢

How much money?

a.

35 ¢

_______ ¢

b.

_______ ¢

_______ ¢

Ring the correct group of coins.

c.

d.

Use with text pages 173–174.

name

PRACTICE

WORKSHEET **55**

Problem Solving • Do You Have Enough Money?

Write how much money.

Do you have enough?

Ring YES or NO.

a.

25 ¢

YES NO

b.

_____ ¢

YES NO

c.

_____ ¢

YES NO

d.

_____ ¢

YES NO

e.

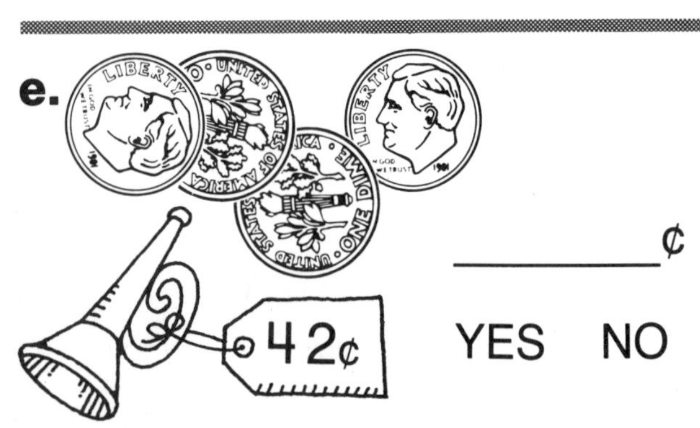

_____ ¢

YES NO

f.

_____ ¢

YES NO

g.

_____ ¢

YES NO

h.

_____ ¢

YES NO

name

PRACTICE

WORKSHEET 56 A

Half-dollar

half-dollar

1¢ 5¢ 10¢ 25¢ 50¢
50 cents

How much money?

a.

60 ¢

______ ¢

b.

______ ¢

______ ¢

Ring how much money is needed.

c.

d.

Go on to Worksheet 56B.

Use with text pages 177–178.

name

PRACTICE

WORKSHEET **56 B**

Half-dollar

Ring how much money is needed.

a.

b.

c.

63¢

d.

Problem Solving

Write how many of each coin are needed to make 40¢.

e.

 ______

 ______

 ______

name

PRACTICE

WORKSHEET **57**

Dollar

1¢	5¢	10¢	25¢	50¢

$0.01	$0.05	$0.10	$0.25	$0.50

100 cents 100¢  1 dollar $1.00

Write the amount in two ways.

a.  150¢ $1.50

b.  ________¢ $________

c.  ________¢ $________

d.  ________¢ $________

e.  ________¢ $________

f.  ________¢ $________

name

PRACTICE

WORKSHEET **58**

Money Practice

Write how much money.

a.

$1.60

b.

$ ______

c.

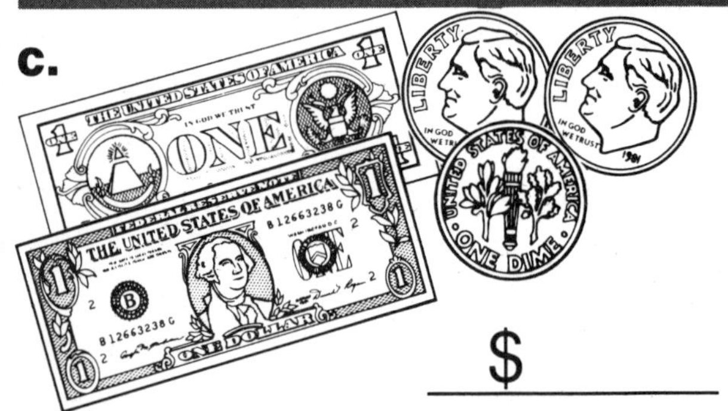

$ ______

d.

$ ______

e.

$ ______

f.

$ ______

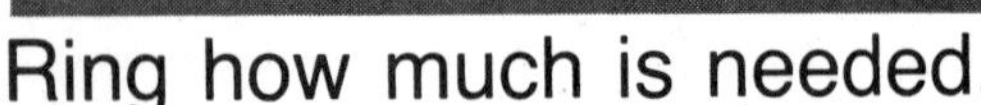

Ring how much is needed.

g.

h.

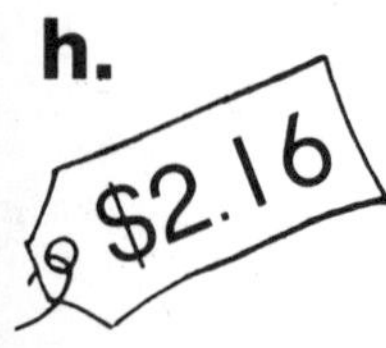

Use with text pages 181–182.

name

PRACTICE

Problem Solving • How Much Money Is Left?

Write how much money.
Cross out what is spent.
Write how much is left.

a.

William has 65 ¢.

He buys 35¢ .

He has 30 ¢ left.

b.

Maggie has ________ ¢.

She buys 21¢ .

She has ________ ¢ left.

c.

Jason has $ ________ .

He buys $2.20 .

He has $ ________ left.

d.

Dawn has $ ________ .

She buys $1.15 .

She has $ ________ left.

Use with text pages 183–184.

name

PRACTICE

WORKSHEET **60**

Adding Two-Digit Numbers

Step 1

Add the ones.

start ↓

tens	ones
2	3
+4	5
	8

Step 2

Add the tens.

tens	ones
2	3
+4	5
6	

Add.

a.

tens	ones
4	2
+1	5
5	7

tens	ones
3	6
+4	0

tens	ones
5	1
+	8

tens	ones
2	4
+6	2

b. $47 + 21$ $\quad 23 + 56$ $\quad 40 + 50$ $\quad 37 + 32$ $\quad 54 + 41$ $\quad 72 + 20$

c. $25 + 74$ $\quad 82 + 6$ $\quad 64 + 12$ $\quad 31 + 56$ $\quad 10 + 60$ $\quad 52 + 34$

d. $61 + 5$ $\quad 20 + 30$ $\quad 78 + 11$ $\quad 45 + 43$ $\quad 22 + 55$ $\quad 92 + 4$

name

Regrouping Ones as Tens

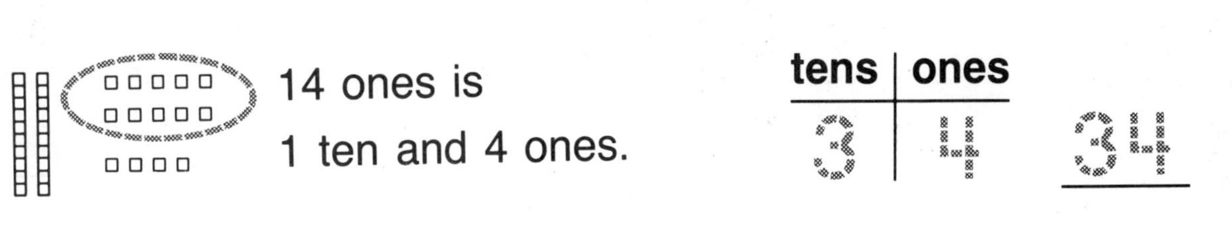

14 ones is
1 ten and 4 ones.
tens | ones
3 | 4
34

Regroup ten ones to make one more ten.
Write the numbers.

a.

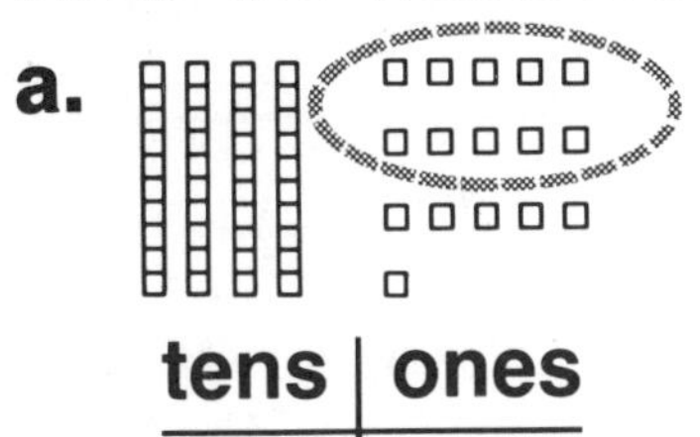

tens	ones
5	6

56

b.

tens	ones

______

c.

tens	ones

______

d.

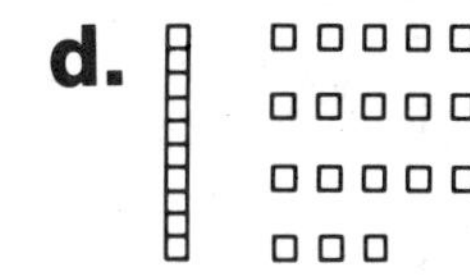

tens	ones

______

e.

tens	ones

______

f.

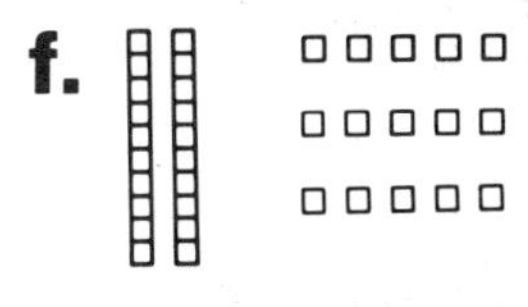

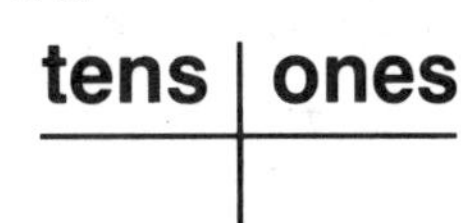

______

g.

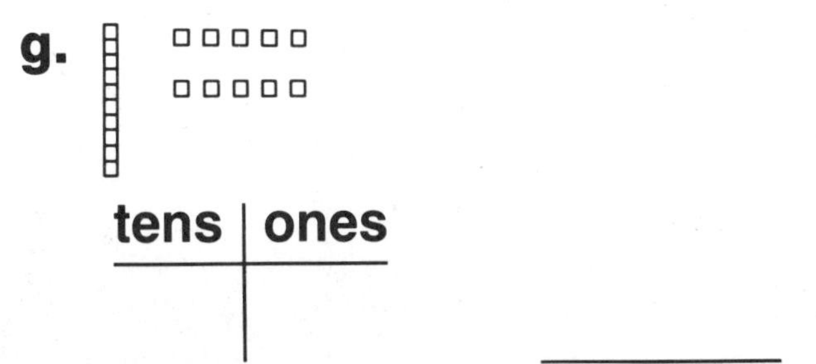

______

h.

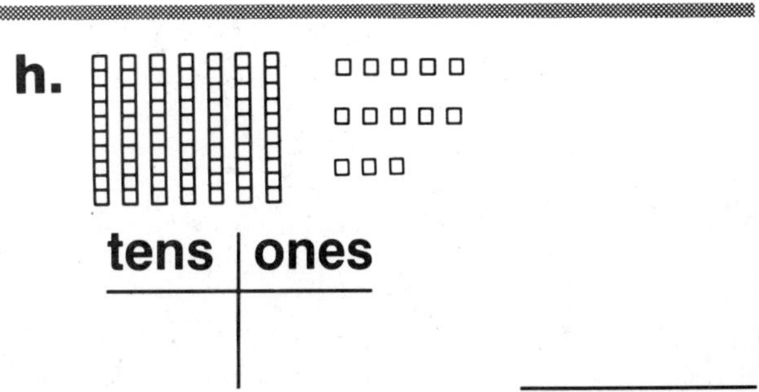

______

Use with text pages 197–198.

name

PRACTICE

WORKSHEET **62**

Addition with Regrouping

Step 1

Add the ones.
Regroup.

start ↓

tens	ones
1	
5	6
+2	8
	4

Step 2

Add the tens.

tens	ones
1	
5	6
+2	8
8	4

Add.

a.

tens	ones
1	
3	7
+4	5
8	2

tens	ones
5	9
+3	3

tens	ones
4	8
+1	7

tens	ones
5	3
+2	8

b. 66 + 16   75 + 9   46 + 29   44 + 38   25 + 55   58 + 8

c. 73 + 19   87 + 5   35 + 39   67 + 14   22 + 18   71 + 19

d. 36 + 47   23 + 49   34 + 26   57 + 13   15 + 56   52 + 29

name

PRACTICE

WORKSHEET **63**

Addition Practice

Add.

	Regrouping		No Regrouping			
a.	57 + 19 = 76		34 + 25 = 59		48 + 13	26 + 42
b.	58 + 27	84 + 9	93 + 6	50 + 37	74 + 18	45 + 27
c.	18 + 25	15 + 12	32 + 48	38 + 40	83 + 5	29 + 16
d.	61 + 27	36 + 47	60 + 10	27 + 3	53 + 14	28 + 48
e.	57 + 9	36 + 38	43 + 22	64 + 5	35 + 48	14 + 2

Problem Solving

Solve.

f. Lee has 27 tomato plants. She plants 24 more. How many tomato plants in all?

g. Juan plants 33 carrot seeds. He plants 16 more. How many carrot seeds in all?

name

PRACTICE

WORKSHEET **64 A**

More Two-Digit Addition

Step 1	**Step 2**
Add the ones. Regroup. **start** ↓	Add the tens.
$\begin{array}{r} {}^{1}\\ 35 \\ +47 \\ \hline 2 \end{array}$	$\begin{array}{r} {}^{1}\\ 35 \\ +47 \\ \hline 82 \end{array}$

Add.

a.	$\begin{array}{r} {}^{1}\\ 54 \\ +38 \\ \hline 92 \end{array}$	$\begin{array}{r} 66 \\ +25 \\ \hline \end{array}$	$\begin{array}{r} 48 \\ +32 \\ \hline \end{array}$	$\begin{array}{r} 73 \\ +\ \ 8 \\ \hline \end{array}$	$\begin{array}{r} 25 \\ +45 \\ \hline \end{array}$	$\begin{array}{r} 36 \\ +58 \\ \hline \end{array}$
b.	$\begin{array}{r} 67 \\ +27 \\ \hline \end{array}$	$\begin{array}{r} 22 \\ +69 \\ \hline \end{array}$	$\begin{array}{r} 64 \\ +\ \ 7 \\ \hline \end{array}$	$\begin{array}{r} 33 \\ +29 \\ \hline \end{array}$	$\begin{array}{r} 28 \\ +42 \\ \hline \end{array}$	$\begin{array}{r} 26 \\ +\ \ 7 \\ \hline \end{array}$
c.	$\begin{array}{r} 15 \\ +38 \\ \hline \end{array}$	$\begin{array}{r} 43 \\ +37 \\ \hline \end{array}$	$\begin{array}{r} 57 \\ +\ \ 4 \\ \hline \end{array}$	$\begin{array}{r} 39 \\ +52 \\ \hline \end{array}$	$\begin{array}{r} 35 \\ +46 \\ \hline \end{array}$	$\begin{array}{r} 21 \\ +\ \ 9 \\ \hline \end{array}$
d.	$\begin{array}{r} 23 \\ +49 \\ \hline \end{array}$	$\begin{array}{r} 34 \\ +19 \\ \hline \end{array}$	$\begin{array}{r} 14 \\ +\ \ 8 \\ \hline \end{array}$	$\begin{array}{r} 16 \\ +44 \\ \hline \end{array}$	$\begin{array}{r} 58 \\ +34 \\ \hline \end{array}$	$\begin{array}{r} 17 \\ +56 \\ \hline \end{array}$

Go on to Worksheet 64B.

Use with text pages 205–206.

name

PRACTICE

WORKSHEET 64 B

More Two-Digit Numbers

Find the sums.

Color sums 60 or less red.

Color sums 61 or more yellow.

23 + 17 = 40	39 + 33	27 + 9	29 + 57	36 + 14	49 + 29
26 + 68	19 + 39	15 + 58	48 + 8	47 + 17	16 + 28
15 + 18	37 + 48	28 + 19	27 + 34	27 + 26	35 + 45

Problem Solving

Solve.

a. The sports store has 25 blue shirts. It has 36 yellow shirts. How many shirts in all?

b. There are 18 blue baseball caps. There are 37 yellow baseball caps. How many baseball caps in all?

c. The store has 15 small fishing rods. It has 19 large fishing rods. How many fishing rods in all?

d. There are 44 tennis balls. 26 more are found. How many tennis balls in all?

name

PRACTICE

WORKSHEET **65**

Three Addends

Step 1 Add the ones.	Step 2 Add the tens.	Step 1 Add the ones. Regroup.	Step 2 Add the tens.
22 23 +24 9	22 23 +24 69	1 12 27 +35 4	12 27 +35 74

Add.

a.	1 24 10 +48 82	32 54 + 3	15 21 +17	30 24 +15	25 14 +37	35 12 +20
b.	34 14 +21	36 43 + 2	25 13 +47	23 14 +22	37 12 +29	41 17 + 6
c.	32 47 +15	20 15 +44	11 35 + 7	24 53 + 9	37 10 +12	44 12 +28

Use with text pages 207–208.

name

PRACTICE

WORKSHEET **66**

Regrouping Ones and Tens

Step 1 Add the ones.	Step 2 Add the tens. Regroup.	Step 1 Add the ones. Regroup.	Step 2 Add the tens. Regroup.
63 +74 7	63 +74 137	1 48 +95 3	1 48 +95 143

Add.

a.	82 + 72 = 154	91 + 54	63 + 44	32 + 84	24 + 90	53 + 53
b.	62 + 75	91 + 95	73 + 91	62 + 93	86 + 91	62 + 86
c.	35 + 96 = 131 (regrouped 1)	84 + 68	48 + 93	85 + 87	94 + 59	55 + 68
d.	95 + 89	77 + 84	76 + 78	57 + 86	97 + 75	78 + 42
e.	96 + 67	36 + 86	56 + 99	44 + 67	89 + 72	88 + 26

name

PRACTICE

WORKSHEET **67**

Addition Sentences

37 + 48 = ____ 37 + 48 = 85 $\begin{array}{r} {}^{1} \\ 37 \\ +48 \\ \hline 85 \end{array}$	56 + 8 = ____ 56 + 8 = 64 $\begin{array}{r} {}^{1} \\ 56 \\ +\ 8 \\ \hline 64 \end{array}$

Add.

a. 43 + 19 = 62 $\begin{array}{r} 43 \\ +19 \\ \hline 62 \end{array}$

b. 37 + 48 = ____

c. 50 + 25 = ____

d. 76 + 7 = ____

e. 63 + 8 = ____

f. 47 + 19 = ____

g. 43 + 15 = ____

h. 72 + 9 = ____

i. 37 + 24 = ____

j. 45 + 28 = ____

name

PRACTICE

WORKSHEET **68**

Checking Addition

Change the order of the addends to check your answer.

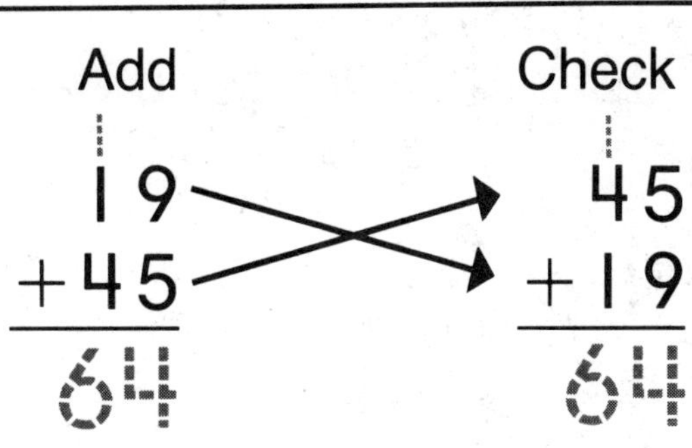

The sums are the same.

Add. Check your answers.

a. 64 + 29 = 93 (check: 29 + 64 = 93) | 37 + 23 (check: 23 + 37) | 45 + 17

b. 48 + 5 | 34 + 52 | 27 + 37

c. 56 + 7 | 14 + 28 | 33 + 12

d. 37 + 58 | 46 + 28 | 34 + 4

e. 28 + 60 | 39 + 43 | 55 + 9

name

PRACTICE

WORKSHEET **69**

Adding Money

Add.

a.

60¢	46¢	54¢	68¢	49¢	25¢
+25¢	+19¢	+40¢	+ 5¢	+37¢	+25¢
85¢	65¢				

b.

29¢	14¢	46¢	58¢	37¢	40¢
+19¢	+43¢	+23¢	+18¢	+ 5¢	+21¢

c.

78¢	23¢	39¢	12¢	34¢	35¢
+ 7¢	+21¢	+14¢	+25¢	+22¢	+35¢

Find the total cost.

d.

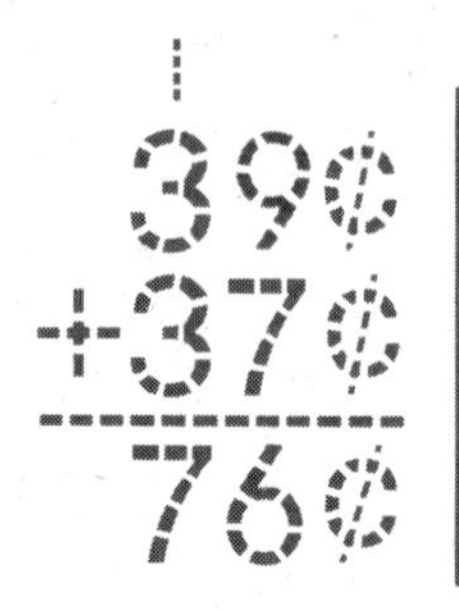

$$\begin{array}{r} 39¢ \\ +37¢ \\ \hline 76¢ \end{array}$$

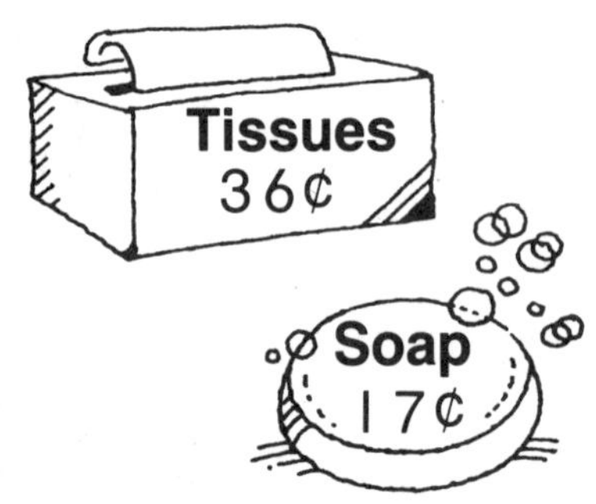

e.

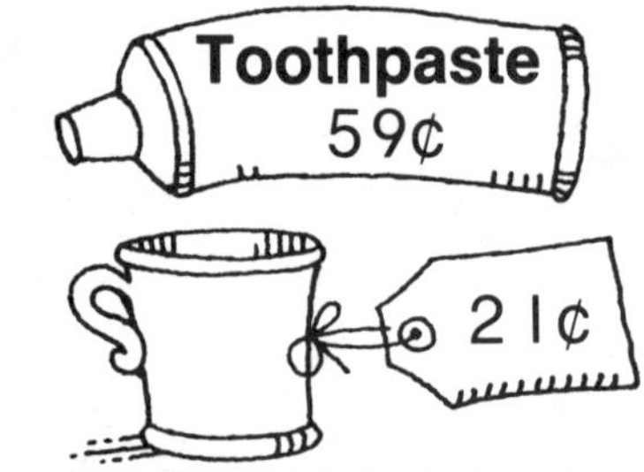

f.

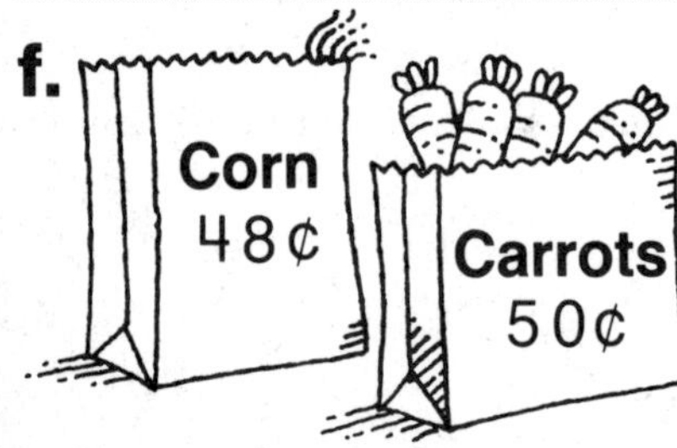

Use with text pages 215–216.

name

PRACTICE

WORKSHEET **70**

Problem Solving • Using Addition

Solve.

a. There are 18 cows in the barn. 26 more cows are outside. How many cows in all?

b. There are 35 chickens outside. 16 more chickens are inside. How many chickens in all?

c. The chickens lay 30 eggs on Monday and 47 on Tuesday. How many eggs in all?

d. 27 hens are in the barn. 29 hens are outside. How many hens in all?

e. The farmer buys 21 bags of feed. He buys 48 more. How many bags of feed in all?

f. The farmer has 12 horses. She buys 8 more horses. How many horses in all?

g. The farm has 89 corn plants. The farmer plants 6 more. How many corn plants in all?

h. There are 63 tomato plants. The farmer plants 28 more. How many tomato plants in all?

name

PRACTICE

WORKSHEET **71**

Subtracting Two-Digit Numbers

Step 1 Subtract the ones.	**Step 2** Subtract the tens.
start ↓	

Step 1 — Subtract the ones. (start ↓ at the ones column)

tens	ones
6	8
−2	7
	1

Step 2 — Subtract the tens.

tens	ones
6	8
−2	7
4	1

Subtract.

a.

tens	ones
7	9
−4	5
3	4

tens	ones
9	8
−6	4

tens	ones
5	6
−	2

tens	ones
7	7
−2	6

b. $85 - 34$ $90 - 40$ $76 - 34$ $63 - 43$ $54 - 23$ $64 - 21$

c. $86 - 30$ $71 - 31$ $56 - 4$ $92 - 71$ $80 - 60$ $47 - 6$

d. $68 - 5$ $75 - 13$ $60 - 10$ $89 - 58$ $59 - 7$ $88 - 46$

name

PRACTICE

WORKSHEET **72**

Regrouping Tens as Ones

Regroup to show one fewer ten and ten more ones.

a.

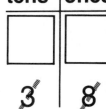

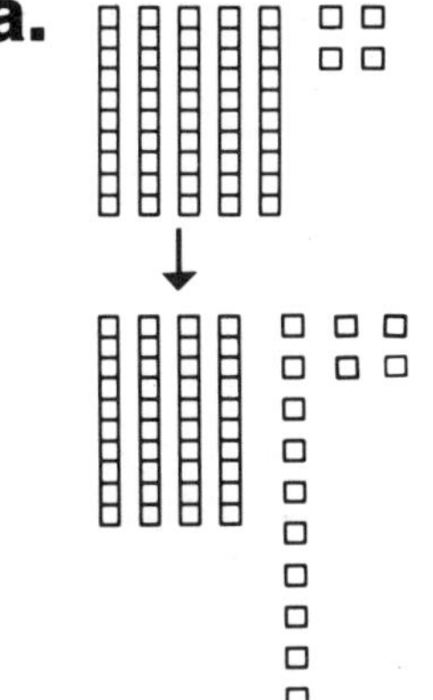

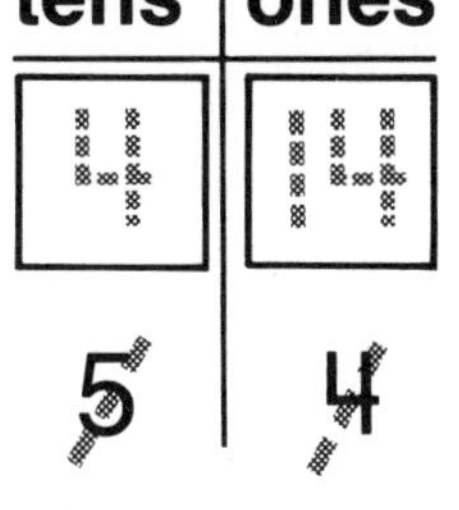

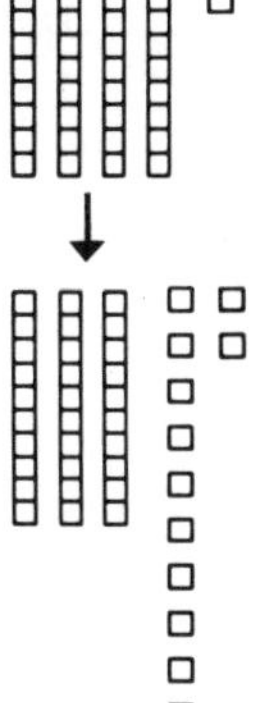

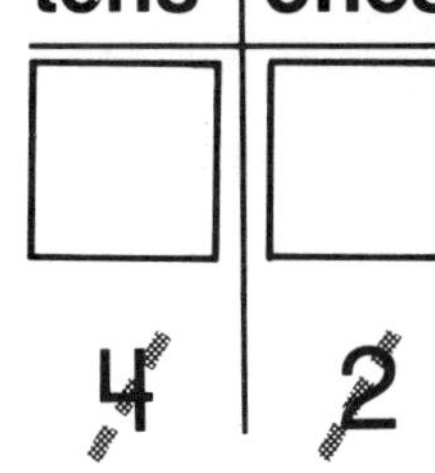

b.

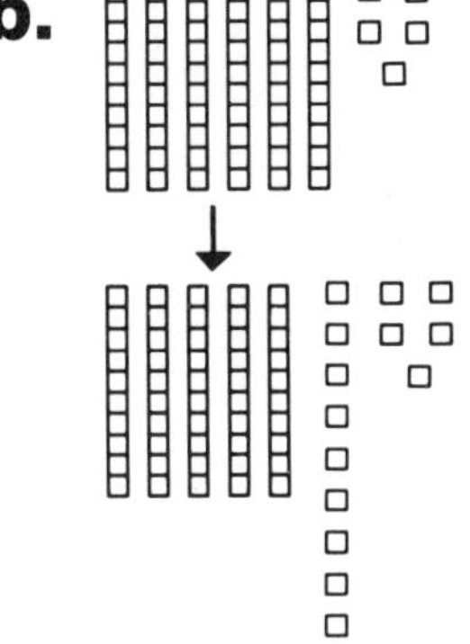

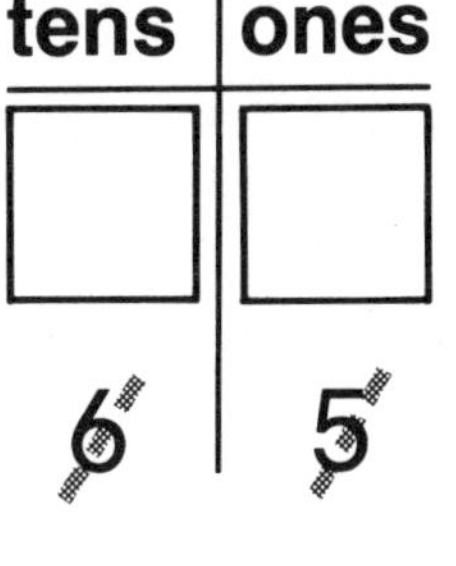

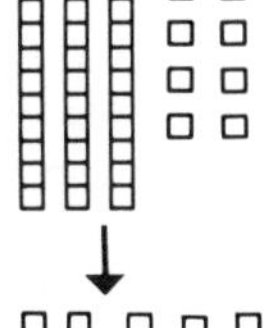

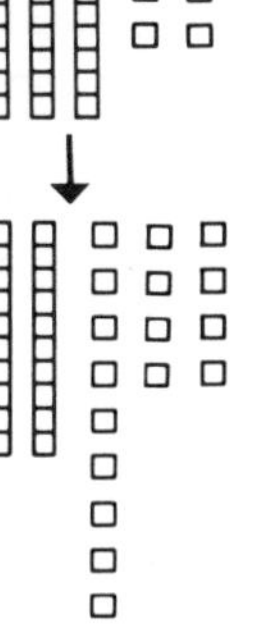

tens	ones
3	8

c.

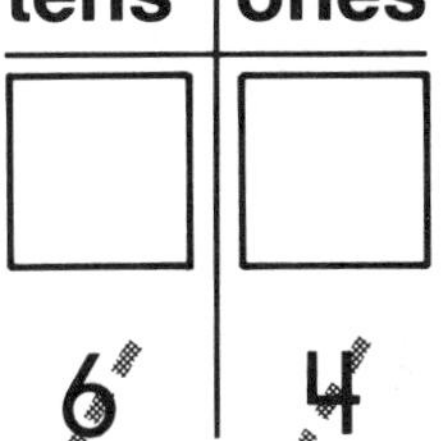

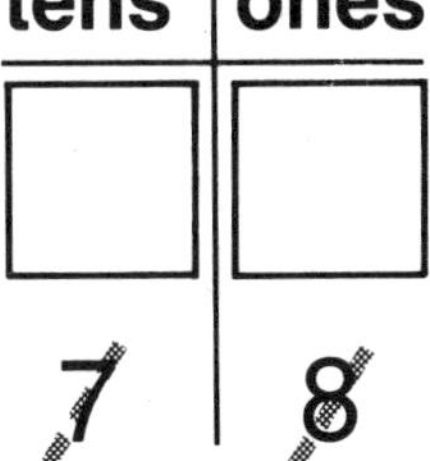

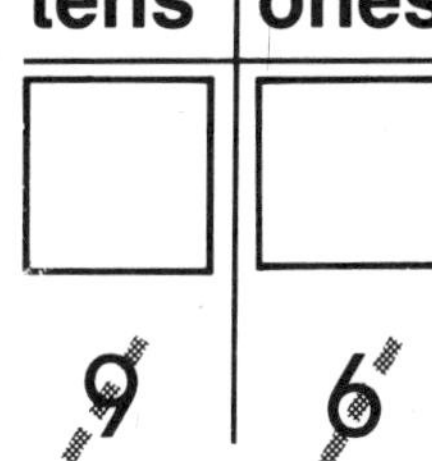

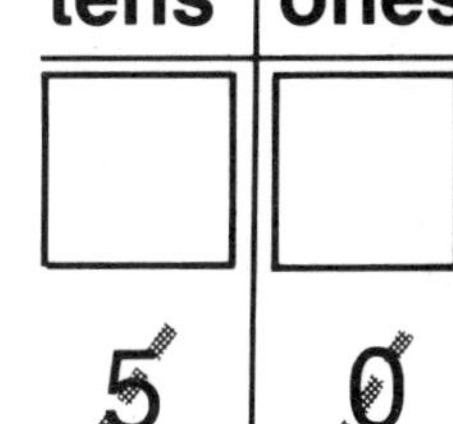

d.

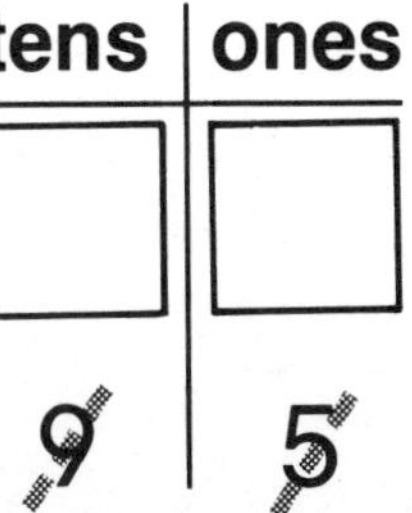

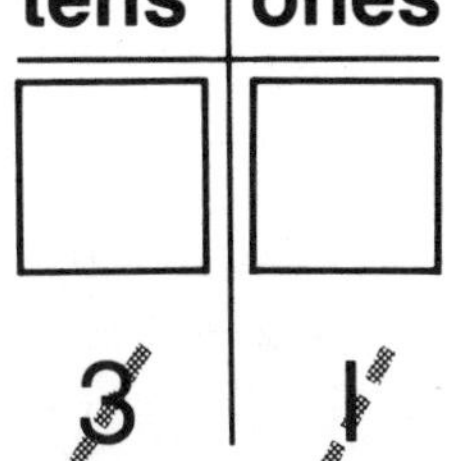

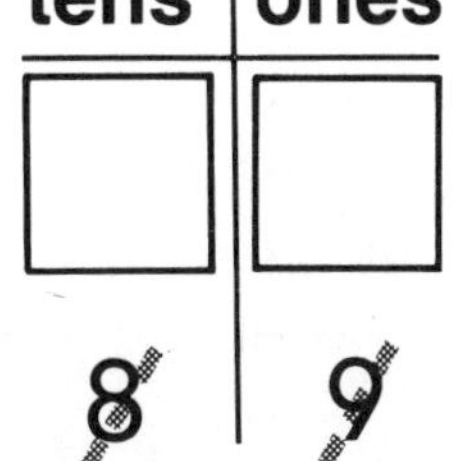

tens	ones
4	2

Use with text pages 231–232.

name

PRACTICE

WORKSHEET 73

Subtraction with Regrouping

Step 1	Step 2	Step 3
You need more ones. Regroup to show one fewer ten and ten more ones.	Subtract the ones.	Subtract the tens.
tens | ones 4 | 16 ~~5~~ | ~~6~~ − 1 | 8	start ↓ tens | ones 4 | 16 ~~5~~ | ~~6~~ − 1 | 8 | 8	tens | ones 4 | 16 ~~5~~ | ~~6~~ − 1 | 8 3 | 8

Subtract.

a.

tens	ones
6	13
~~7~~	~~3~~
−2	5
4	8

tens	ones
4	6
−	7

tens	ones
3	2
−1	8

tens	ones
5	6
−	9

b. $95 - 37$ $67 - 48$ $80 - 7$ $55 - 26$ $91 - 85$ $83 - 69$

c. $78 - 19$ $46 - 7$ $93 - 86$ $52 - 5$ $76 - 58$ $57 - 39$

d. $61 - 3$ $92 - 64$ $85 - 58$ $74 - 18$ $90 - 76$ $44 - 37$

name

PRACTICE

WORKSHEET 74 A

More Subtraction with Regrouping

Step 1	Step 2	Step 3
You need more ones. Regroup.	Subtract the ones.	Subtract the tens.
6 15 ~~7~~~~5~~ −38	6 15 ~~7~~~~5~~ −38 7	6 15 ~~7~~~~5~~ −38 37

Subtract.

a. 5 15 ~~6~~~~5~~ − 47 = 18   83 − 19   62 − 16   78 − 49   44 − 17   45 − 9

b. 77 − 59   56 − 28   74 − 8   61 − 37   52 − 26   50 − 25

c. 36 − 7   53 − 35   48 − 39   30 − 15   42 − 5   67 − 58

d. 40 − 27   95 − 87   31 − 4   85 − 29   75 − 47   43 − 18

Go on to Worksheet 74B.

name

PRACTICE

WORKSHEET 74 B

More Subtraction with Regrouping

Subtract.

Color answers 40 or less blue.

Color answers 41 or more yellow.

50 − 25 = 25	74 − 57	83 − 49	42 − 27	70 − 48	42 − 4
21 − 9	61 − 26	65 − 38	82 − 39	75 − 26	53 − 7
80 − 29	90 − 28	67 − 19	83 − 9	92 − 37	84 − 17

Problem Solving

Solve.

a. The zoo has 42 large turtles. It has 24 small turtles. How many more large turtles than small turtles?

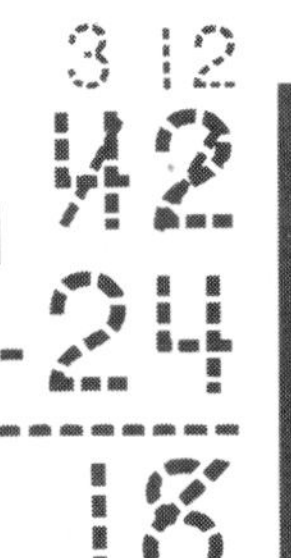

b. The zoo buys 84 bags of food. 37 bags are used. How many bags are left?

c. There are 60 monkeys. There are 23 gorillas. How many more monkeys than gorillas?

d. The zoo has 96 bananas. The monkeys eat 68. How many bananas ae left?

Use with text pages 235–236.

name

PRACTICE

WORKSHEET **75**

Subtraction Practice

There are enough ones. Subtract.	There are not enough ones. Regroup and subtract.
58 − 24 = 34	83 − 47 = 36 (regrouped: 7 tens 13 ones)

Subtract.

a.	64 − 9 = 55 (regrouped: 5 tens 14 ones)	79 − 48	53 − 37	87 − 33	43 − 18	72 − 20
b.	56 − 38	73 − 7	78 − 35	76 − 42	67 − 9	94 − 68
c.	96 − 70	61 − 17	85 − 49	65 − 8	81 − 10	54 − 22
d.	74 − 47	58 − 34	55 − 19	62 − 46	63 − 41	71 − 36
e.	69 − 28	82 − 57	84 − 32	50 − 6	45 − 5	75 − 26

Use with text pages 239–240.

name

PRACTICE

WORKSHEET **76**

Subtraction Sentences

73 − 38 = ____ 73 − 38 = 35	6 13 ~~7~~~~3~~ −38 35
62 − 6 = ____ 62 − 6 = 56	5 12 ~~6~~~~2~~ −6 56

Subtract.

a. 66 − 48 = 18   (5 16 / ~~6~~~~6~~ / −48 / 18)

b. 39 − 15 = ____

c. 89 − 45 = ____

d. 72 − 5 = ____

e. 51 − 16 = ____

f. 51 − 27 = ____

g. 53 − 8 = ____

h. 76 − 48 = ____

i. 44 − 31 = ____

j. 60 − 25 = ____

name

PRACTICE

WORKSHEET **77**

Checking Subtraction

Add to check your answers.

Subtract		Check
6 12		
72	These should be the same.	35
−37		+37
35		72

Subtract. Add to check your answers.

a.	75 −47 = 28 (28 + 47 = 75)	46 − 7 (39 + 7)	64 −23
b.	92 −46	54 − 5	32 −14
c.	45 −18	79 −55	63 −38
d.	62 −12	57 − 9	46 −11
e.	72 − 4	73 −50	50 −33

name

PRACTICE

WORKSHEET **78**

Problem Solving • Using Subtraction

Solve.

a. 46 turtles are in the pond. 38 frogs are in the pond. How many more turtles than frogs are in the pond?

b. There are 38 frogs. 19 frogs hop away. How many frogs are left?

c. 53 ducks are playing. 30 ducks swim away. How many ducks are left?

d. 46 ducks and 29 swans are in the pond. How many more ducks than swans are there?

e. The fish tank has 64 goldfish. It has 37 starfish. How many more goldfish than starfish are there?

f. The fish tank has 70 plants. 27 plants are eaten. How many plants are left?

g. 41 goldfish are eating. 26 goldfish swim away. How many goldfish are still eating?

h. There are 34 yellow flowers and 21 pink flowers. How many more yellow flowers than pink flowers are there?

name

PRACTICE

WORKSHEET **79**

Subtracting Money

Subtract.

a.	94¢ −71¢ 23¢	5 12 62¢ −34¢ 28¢	51¢ −16¢	97¢ − 5¢	76¢ −19¢	50¢ −35¢
b.	68¢ −14¢	60¢ −28¢	75¢ −35¢	84¢ −36¢	72¢ − 7¢	51¢ −20¢
c.	87¢ −39¢	42¢ − 9¢	68¢ −17¢	55¢ −28¢	70¢ −51¢	86¢ −22¢

Find how much is left.

	Had	Bought	Have left
d.	80¢	 67¢	 80¢ −67¢ _____¢
e.	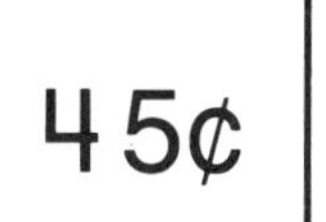 45¢	 36¢	 _____¢
f.	 89¢	 79¢	 _____¢
g.	92¢	 65¢	_____¢

name

PRACTICE

WORKSHEET **80**

Mixed Practice

Add or subtract. Watch the signs.

a.		$\begin{array}{r} \overset{1}{3}8 \\ +45 \\ \hline 83 \end{array}$		$\begin{array}{r} \overset{6}{\not7}\overset{12}{\not2} \\ -35 \\ \hline 37 \end{array}$	$\begin{array}{r} 25 \\ +25 \\ \hline \end{array}$	$\begin{array}{r} 74 \\ -16 \\ \hline \end{array}$
b.	$\begin{array}{r} 56 \\ -\ \ 7 \\ \hline \end{array}$	$\begin{array}{r} 26 \\ +49 \\ \hline \end{array}$	$\begin{array}{r} 75 \\ -36 \\ \hline \end{array}$	$\begin{array}{r} 43 \\ +27 \\ \hline \end{array}$	$\begin{array}{r} 99 \\ -71 \\ \hline \end{array}$	$\begin{array}{r} 80 \\ -47 \\ \hline \end{array}$
c.	$\begin{array}{r} 68 \\ +13 \\ \hline \end{array}$	$\begin{array}{r} 41 \\ -36 \\ \hline \end{array}$	$\begin{array}{r} 47 \\ +30 \\ \hline \end{array}$	$\begin{array}{r} 56 \\ +28 \\ \hline \end{array}$	$\begin{array}{r} 68 \\ -29 \\ \hline \end{array}$	$\begin{array}{r} 38 \\ +\ \ 4 \\ \hline \end{array}$

Problem Solving

Add or subtract to solve the problems.

d. 34 girls and 48 boys are at the school fair. How many children in all?

e. There are 50 prizes. 26 prizes are given away. How many prizes are left?

f. Kathy scored 63 points in a game. Larry scored 45 points. How many more points did Kathy score than Larry?

g. The children sell 26 glasses of grape juice and 36 glasses of orange juice. How many glasses of juice are sold in all?

name

PRACTICE

WORKSHEET **81**

Problem Solving • Adding and Subtracting Money

a.

$$\begin{array}{r} \scriptstyle 1 \\ 45¢ \\ +\,39¢ \\ \hline 84¢ \end{array}$$

What is the total cost?

b.

How much more for than ?

$$\begin{array}{r} \scriptstyle 4\ 13 \\ 53¢ \\ -\,36¢ \\ \hline 17¢ \end{array}$$

c.

How much more for than ?

d.

What is the total cost?

e.

What is the total cost?

f.

How much more for than ?

name

PRACTICE

WORKSHEET **82**

Solid Geometric Shapes

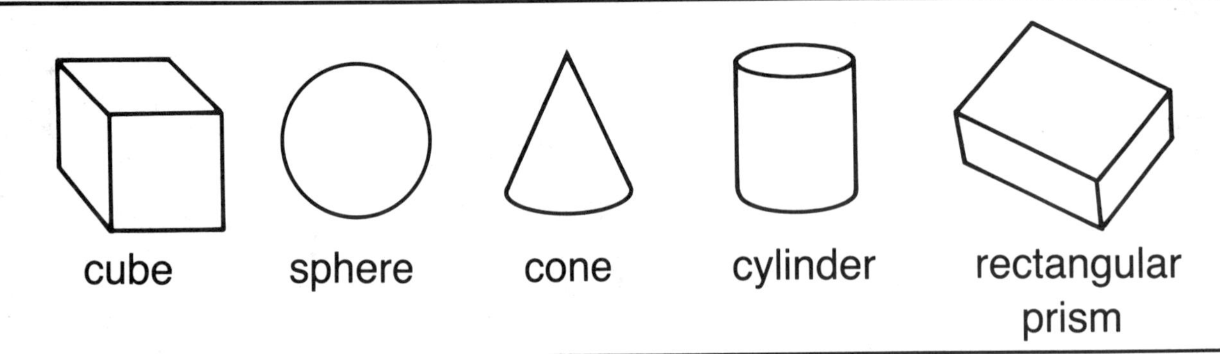

Ring the objects that are the same shape.

a.

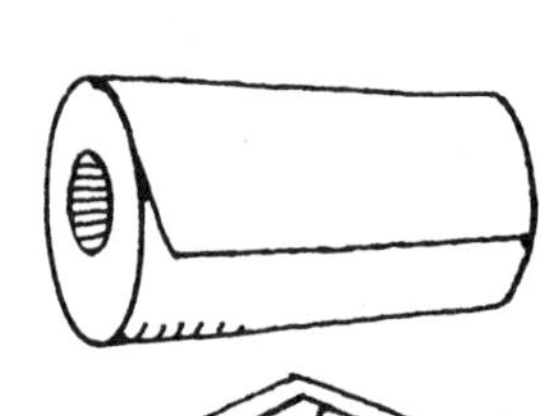

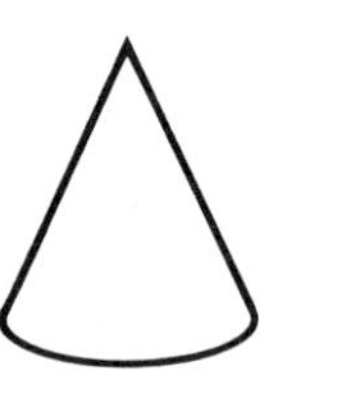

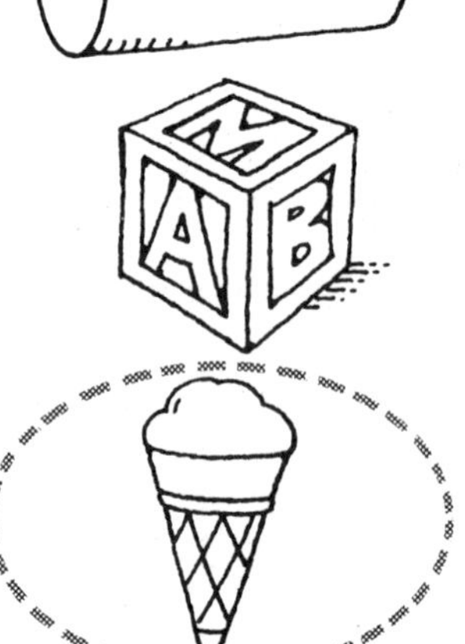

b.

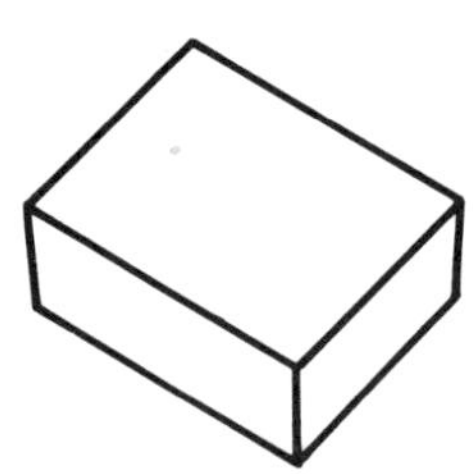

c.

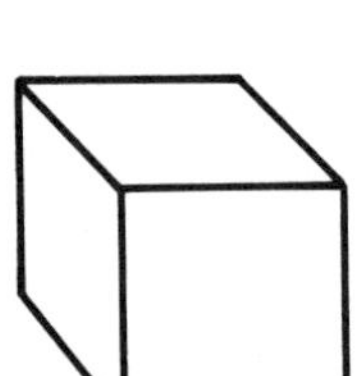

d.

name

PRACTICE

WORKSHEET **83**

Circles, Squares, Triangles, and Rectangles

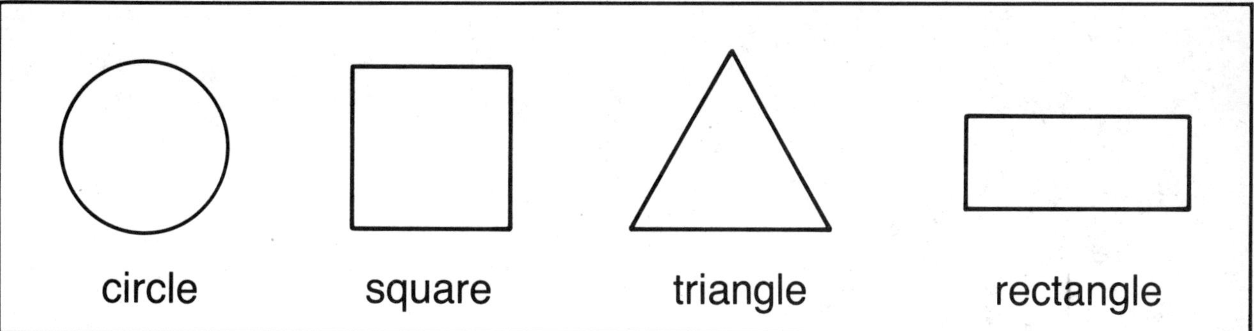

Color

circles red. triangles orange.

squares blue. rectangles green.

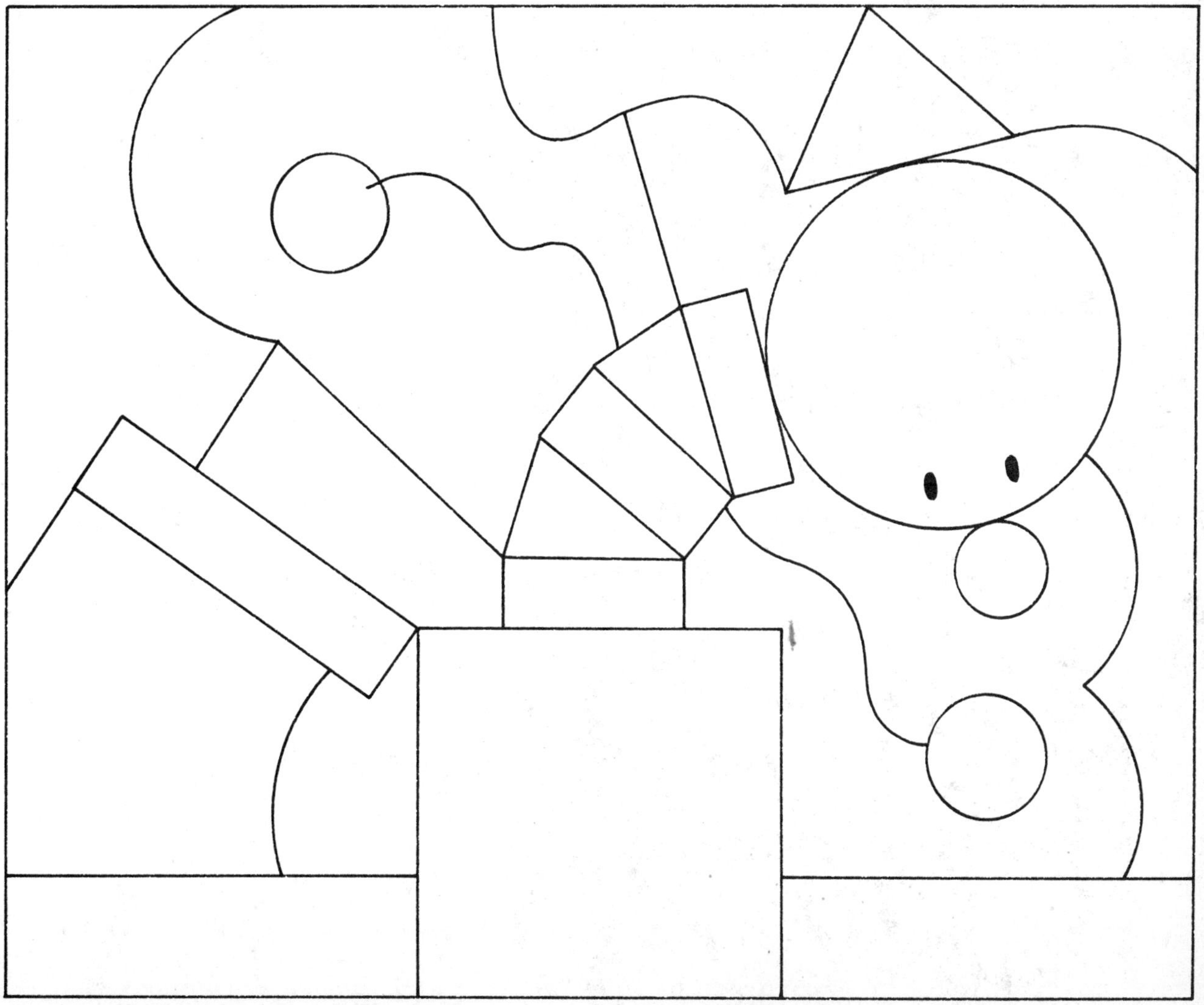

Use with text pages 269–270.

name

PRACTICE

WORKSHEET **84**

Sides and Corners

How many sides and corners?

a.

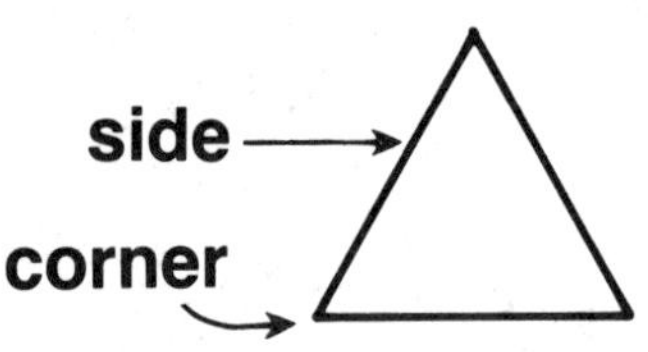

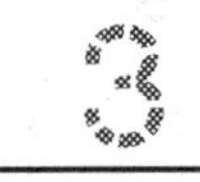 sides

 corners

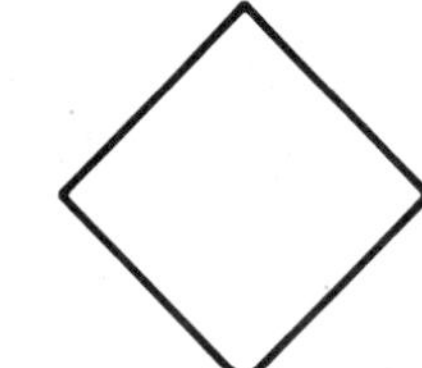

_____ sides

_____ corners

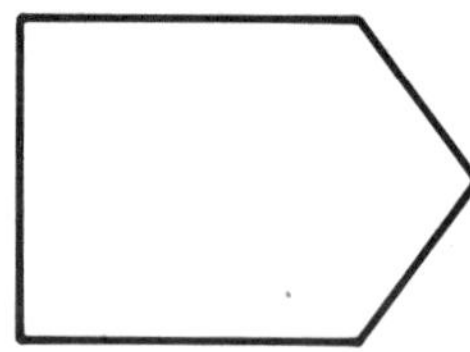

_____ sides

_____ corners

b.

_____ sides

_____ corners

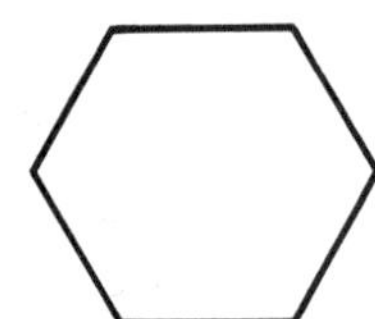

_____ sides

_____ corners

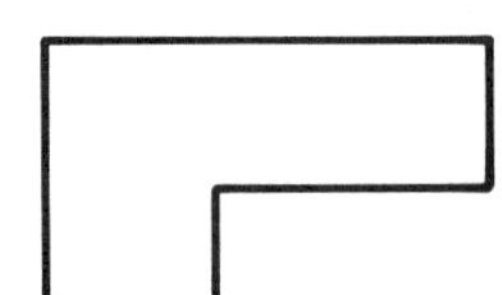

_____ sides

_____ corners

Draw each shape.

c.

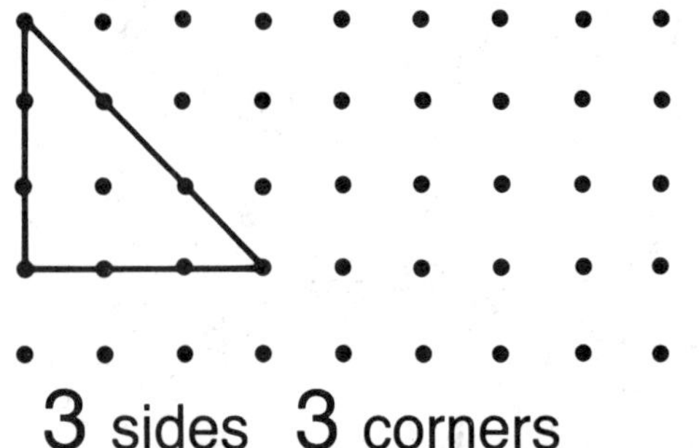

3 sides 3 corners

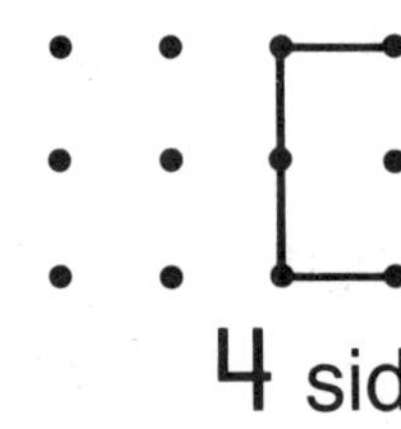

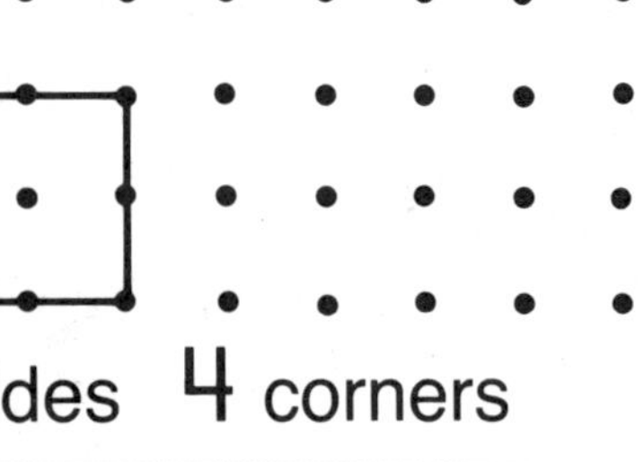

4 sides 4 corners

d.

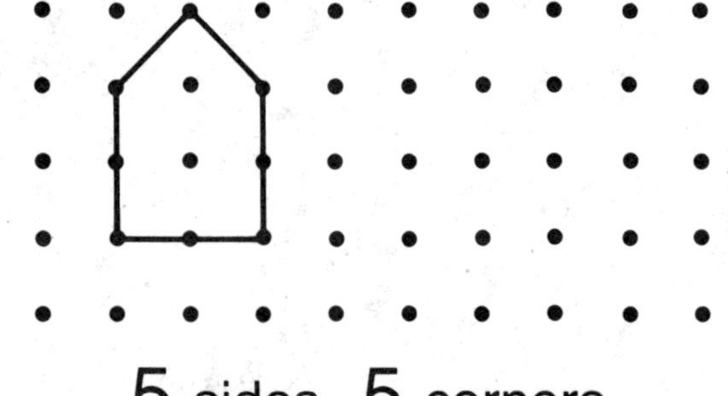

5 sides 5 corners

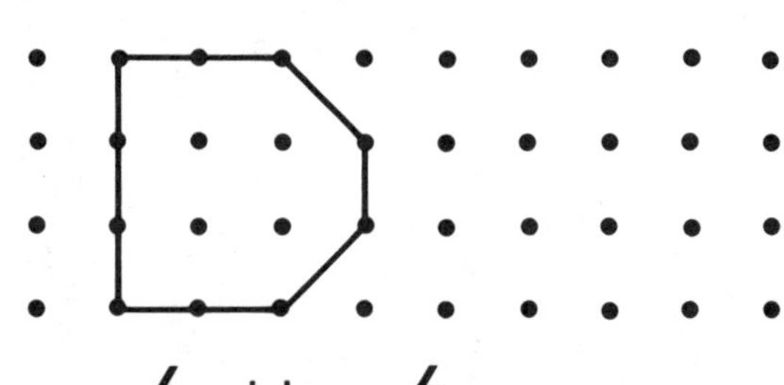

6 sides 6 corners

name

PRACTICE

WORKSHEET **85**

Equal Parts

These two parts match.
They are equal.

These do not match.
They are not equal.

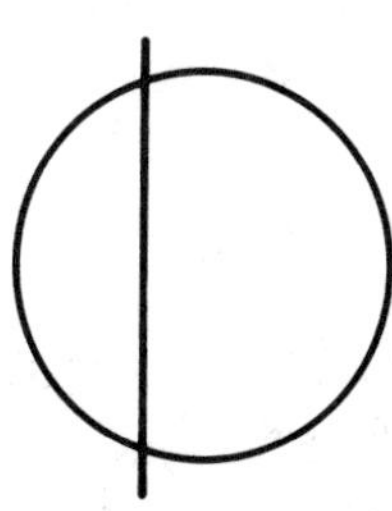

Are the parts equal? Ring YES or NO.

a.

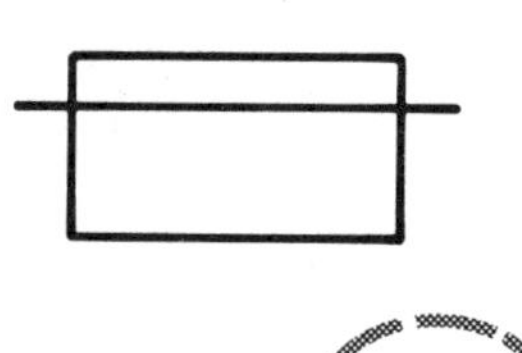

YES NO

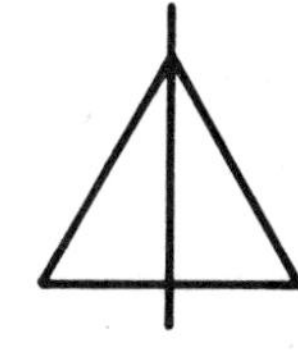

YES NO

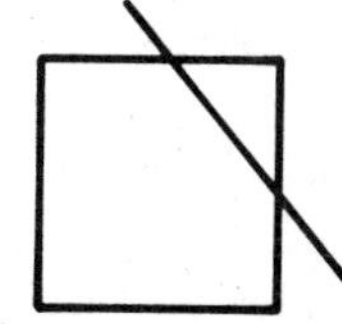

YES NO

b.

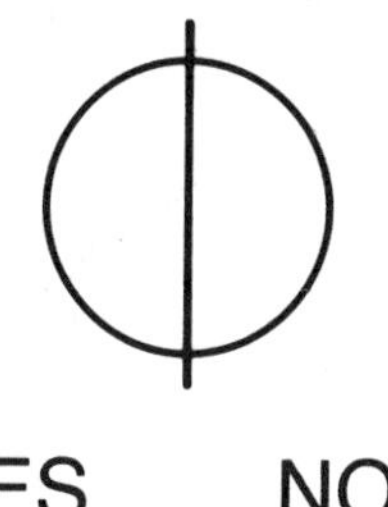

YES NO

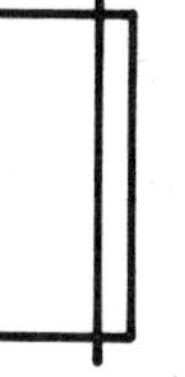

YES NO

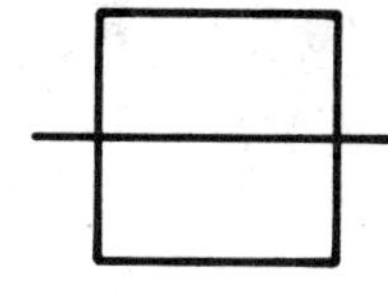

YES NO

Ring the shapes that show equal parts.

c.

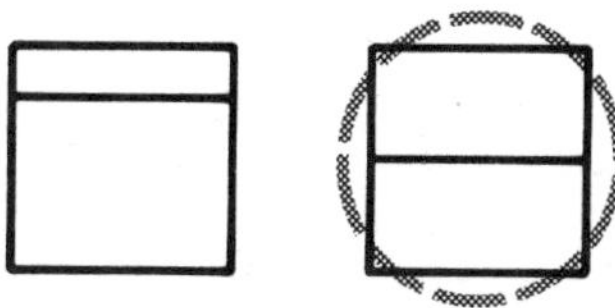

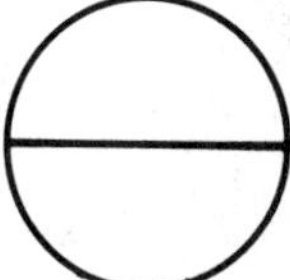

d.

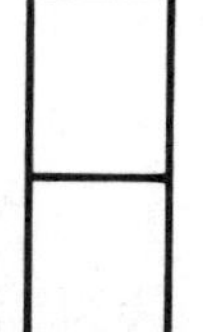
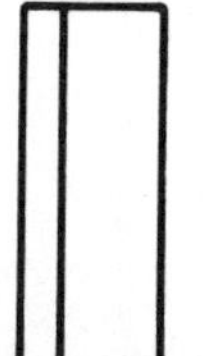

name

PRACTICE

WORKSHEET **86 A**

Fractions

Ring the shapes that show halves.

a. halves

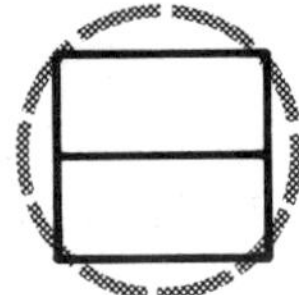   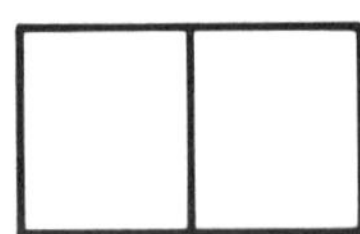 

2 equal parts

Ring the shapes that show thirds.

b. thirds

 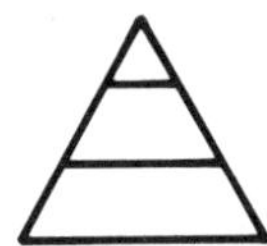 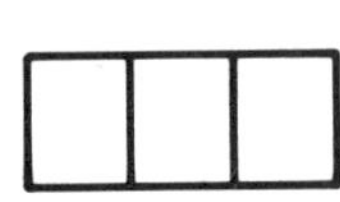  

3 equal parts

Ring the shapes that show fourths.

c. fourths

 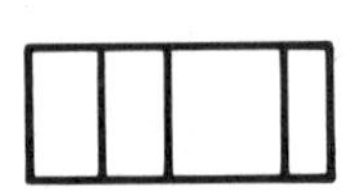   

4 equal parts

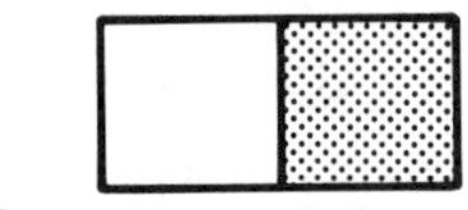

$\frac{1}{2}$ 1 ← part is shaded. 2 ← equal parts in all.

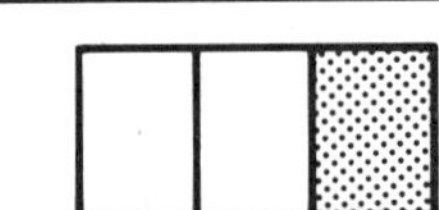

$\frac{1}{3}$ 1 ← part is shaded. 3 ← equal parts in all.

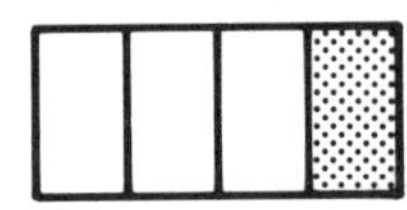

$\frac{1}{4}$ 1 ← part is shaded. 4 ← equal parts in all.

Ring the correct fractions.

d.

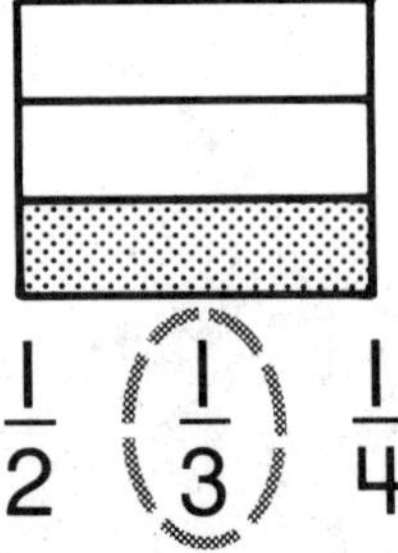

$\frac{1}{2}$ $\frac{1}{3}$ $\frac{1}{4}$

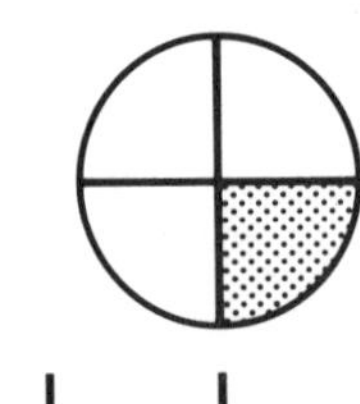

$\frac{1}{2}$ $\frac{1}{3}$ $\frac{1}{4}$

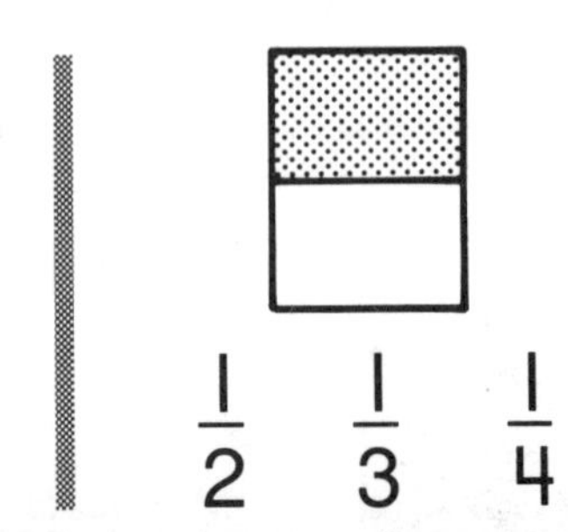

$\frac{1}{2}$ $\frac{1}{3}$ $\frac{1}{4}$

Go on to Worksheet 86B.

Use with text pages 277–278.

name

PRACTICE

WORKSHEET 86 B

Fractions

Ring the correct fractions.

a.

$\frac{1}{2}$ $\frac{1}{3}$ $\frac{1}{4}$

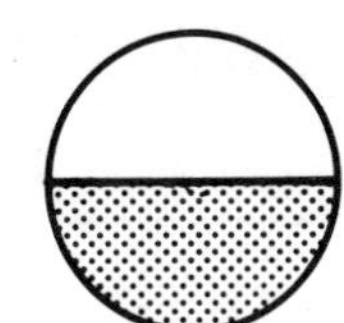

$\frac{1}{2}$ $\frac{1}{3}$ $\frac{1}{4}$

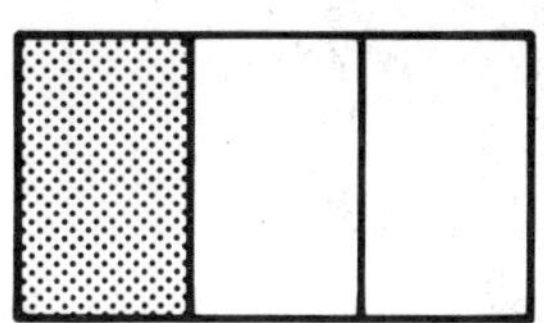

$\frac{1}{2}$ $\frac{1}{3}$ $\frac{1}{4}$

b.

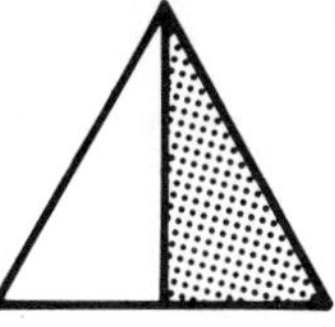

$\frac{1}{2}$ $\frac{1}{3}$ $\frac{1}{4}$

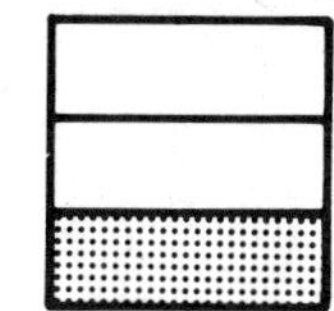

$\frac{1}{2}$ $\frac{1}{3}$ $\frac{1}{4}$

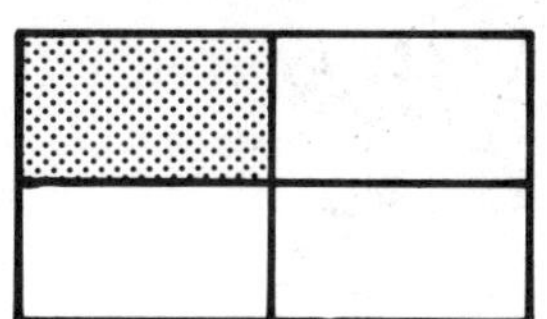

$\frac{1}{2}$ $\frac{1}{3}$ $\frac{1}{4}$

c.

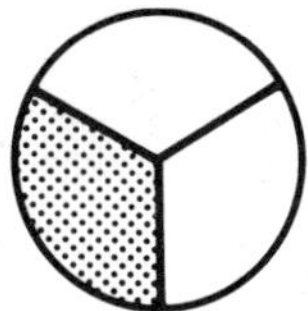

$\frac{1}{2}$ $\frac{1}{3}$ $\frac{1}{4}$

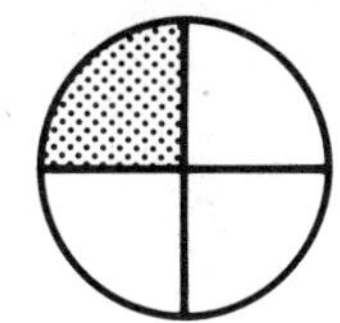

$\frac{1}{2}$ $\frac{1}{3}$ $\frac{1}{4}$

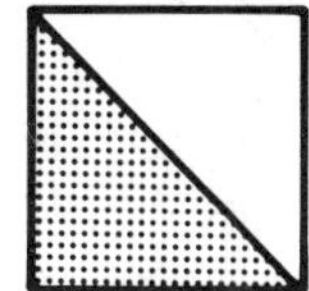

$\frac{1}{2}$ $\frac{1}{3}$ $\frac{1}{4}$

Color.

d.

$\frac{1}{2}$ 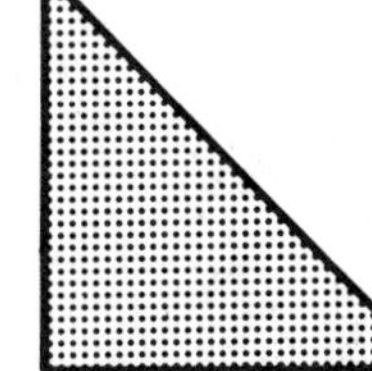

$\frac{1}{4}$ 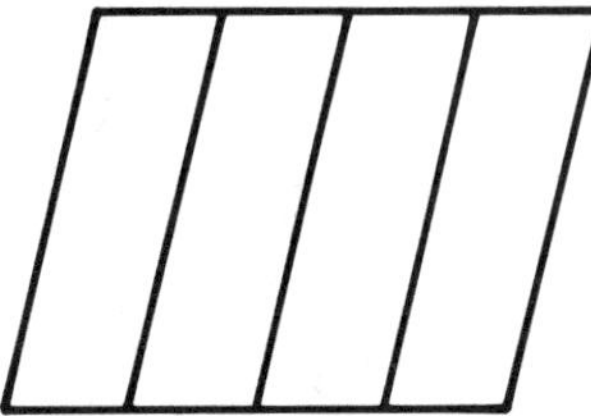

$\frac{1}{3}$ 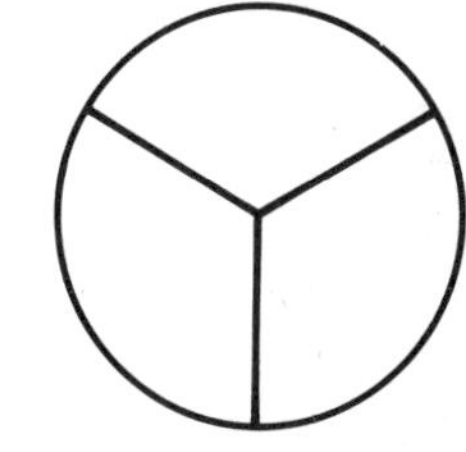

e.

$\frac{1}{3}$ 

$\frac{1}{2}$ 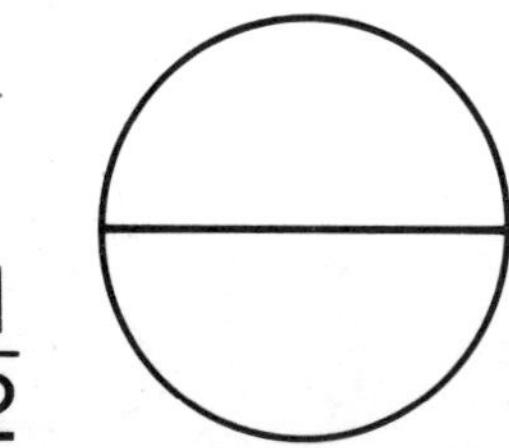

$\frac{1}{4}$

name

PRACTICE

WORKSHEET **87**

More About Fractions

$\frac{2}{3}$ ← parts are shaded. ← equal parts in all.

$\frac{2}{4}$ ← parts are shaded. ← equal parts in all.

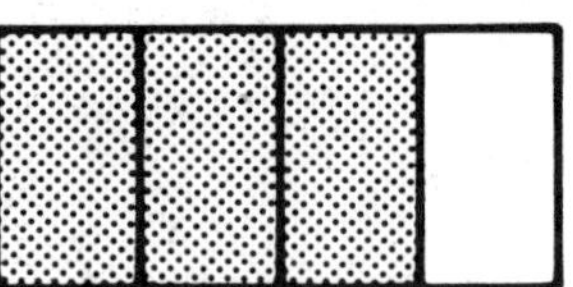

$\frac{3}{4}$ ← parts are shaded. ← equal parts in all.

Ring the correct fractions.

a.

$\frac{1}{3}$ $\frac{2}{3}$ $\frac{1}{4}$

$\frac{1}{2}$ $\frac{2}{4}$ $\frac{3}{4}$

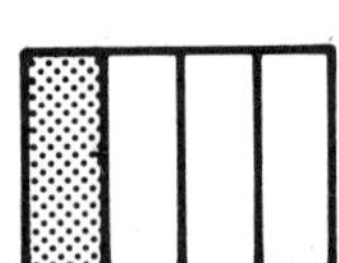

$\frac{1}{4}$ $\frac{2}{4}$ $\frac{3}{4}$

b.

$\frac{1}{2}$ $\frac{1}{3}$ $\frac{1}{4}$

$\frac{2}{3}$ $\frac{2}{4}$ $\frac{3}{4}$

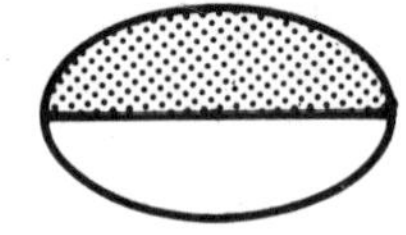

$\frac{1}{2}$ $\frac{1}{3}$ $\frac{2}{3}$

Color.

c.

$\frac{1}{4}$ 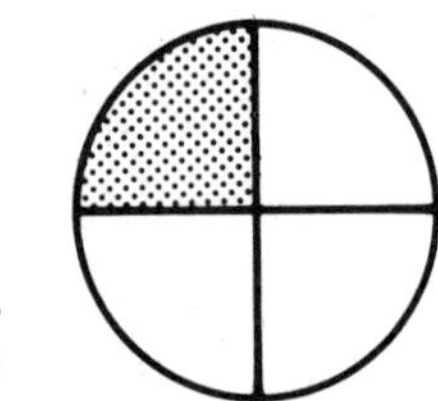

$\frac{2}{3}$ 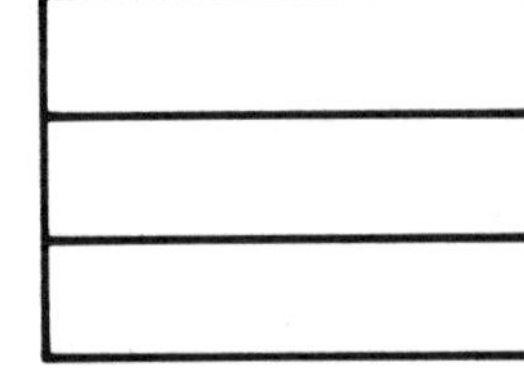

$\frac{3}{4}$ 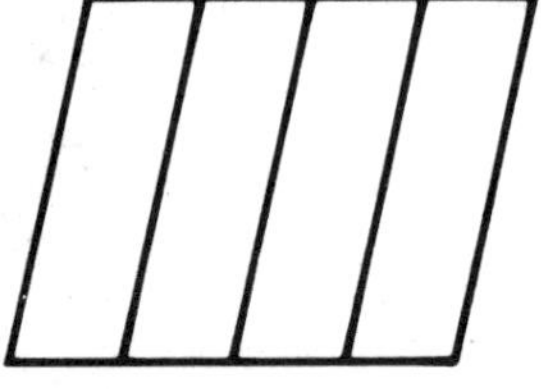

d.

$\frac{1}{2}$ 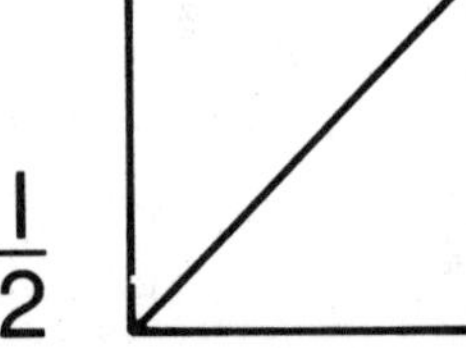

$\frac{2}{4}$ 

$\frac{1}{3}$ 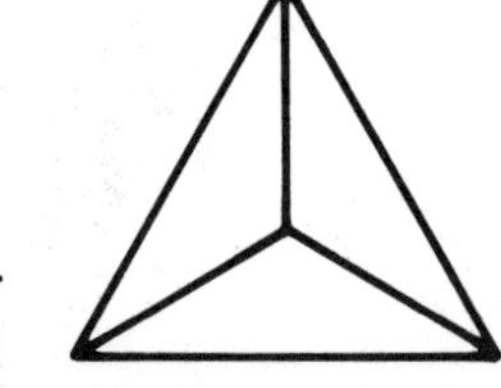

name

PRACTICE

WORKSHEET **88**

Writing Fractions

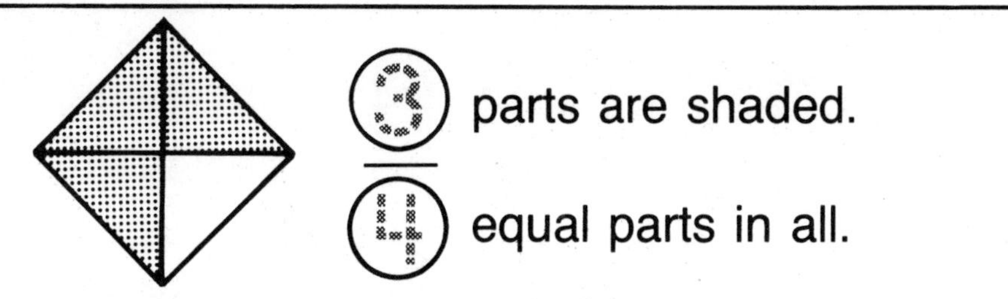

Write the fraction that tells what part is shaded.

a.

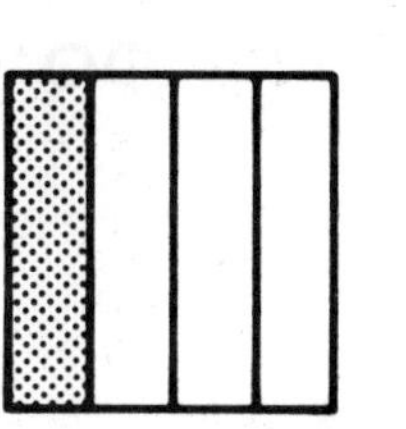

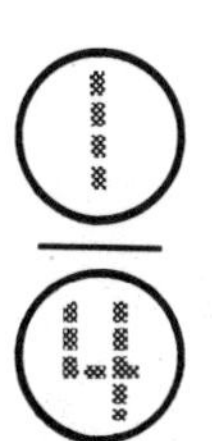

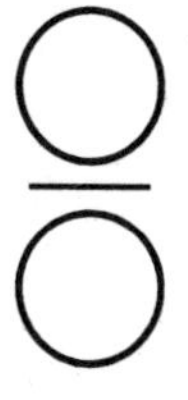

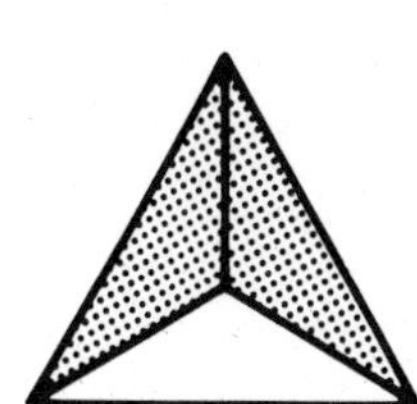

b.

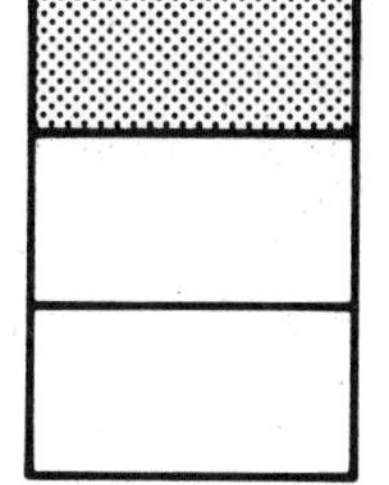

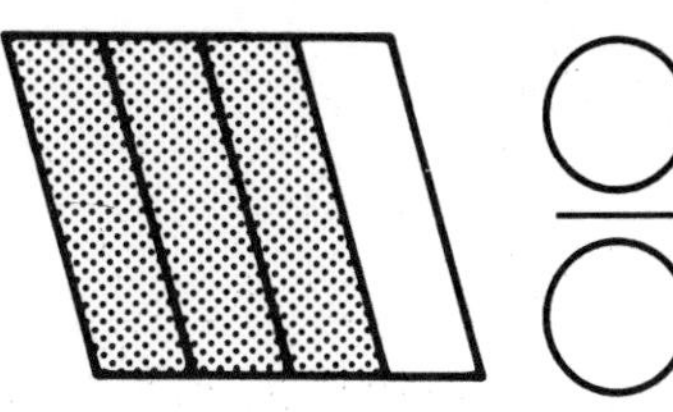

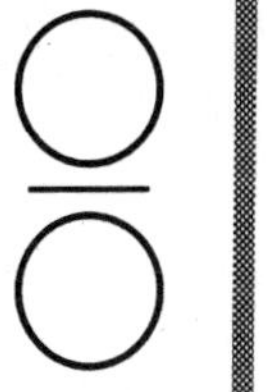

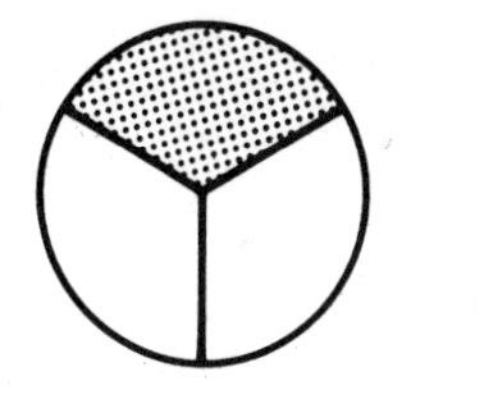

c.

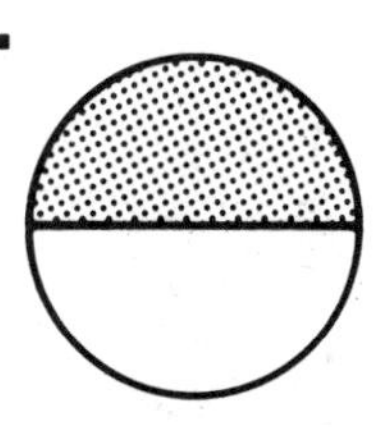

$\frac{1}{2}$ ____

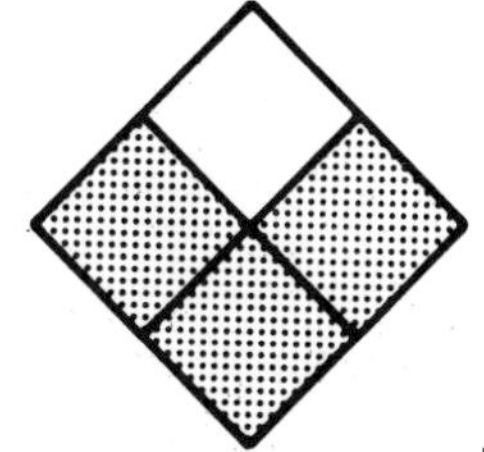

____

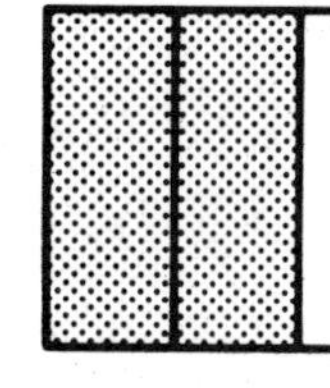

____

d.

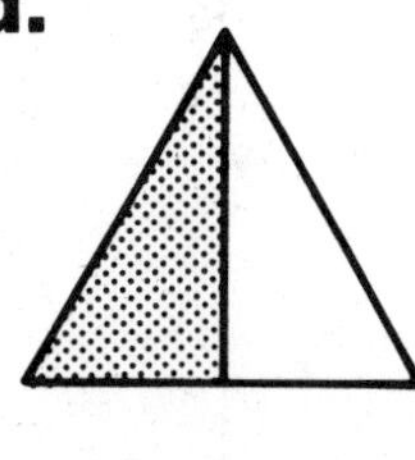

____

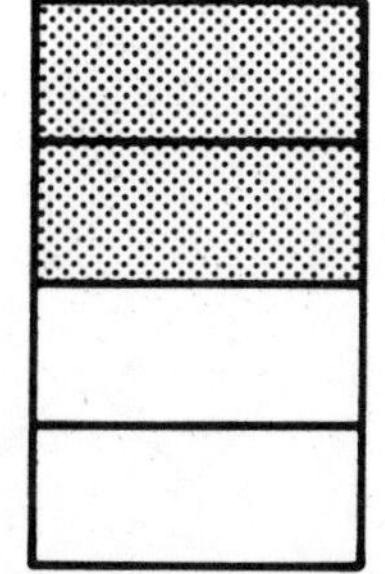

____

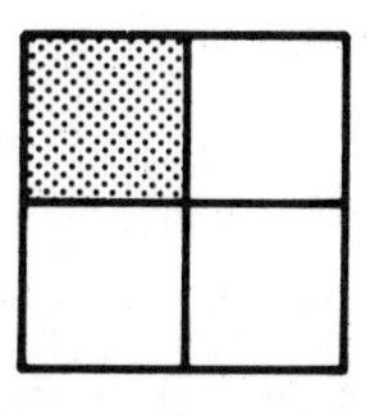

____

Use with text pages 281–282.

name

PRACTICE

WORKSHEET **89**

Parts of Groups

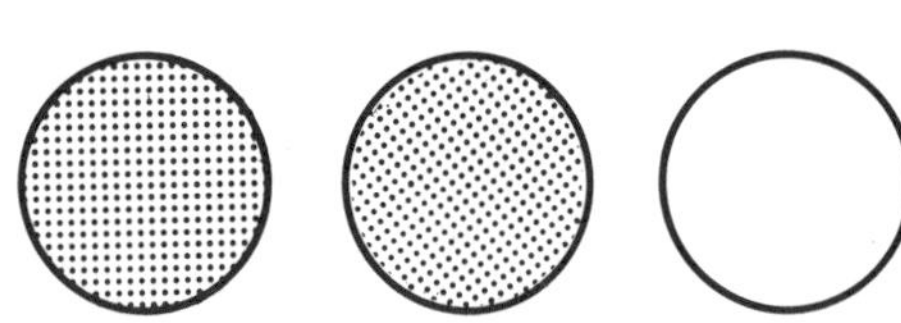

$\frac{2}{3}$ 2 ← circles are shaded.
3 ← circles in all.

Ring the fraction that tells what part of the group is shaded.

a.

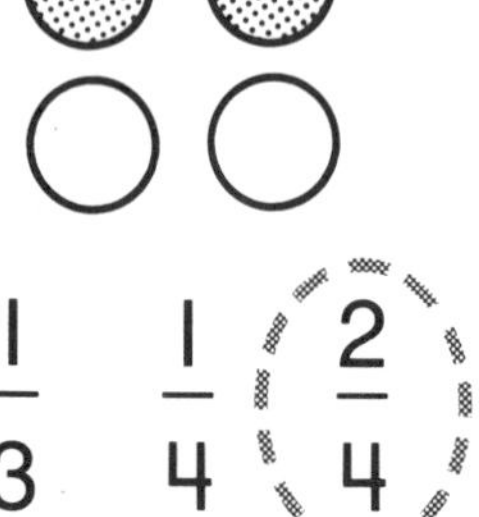

$\frac{1}{3}$ $\frac{1}{4}$ $\frac{2}{4}$

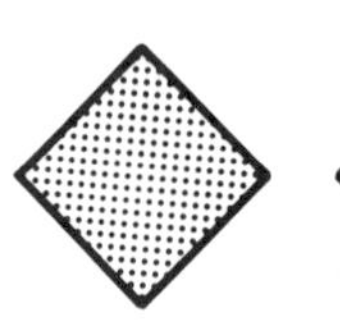

$\frac{1}{2}$ $\frac{1}{3}$ $\frac{1}{4}$

$\frac{2}{4}$ $\frac{3}{4}$ $\frac{2}{3}$

b.

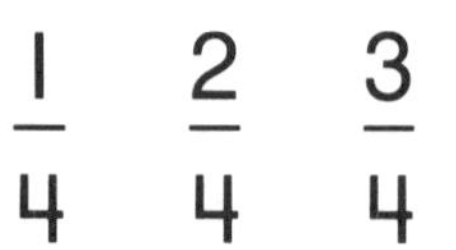

$\frac{1}{4}$ $\frac{2}{4}$ $\frac{3}{4}$

$\frac{1}{2}$ $\frac{1}{3}$ $\frac{2}{3}$

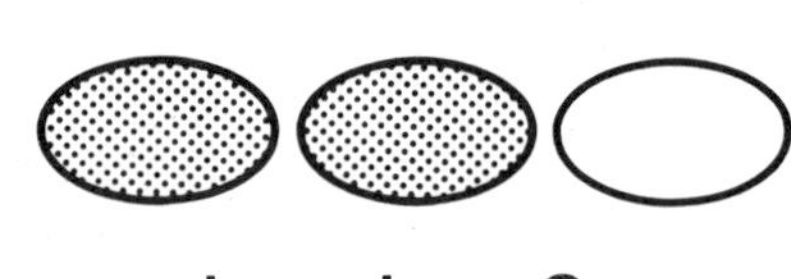

$\frac{1}{4}$ $\frac{1}{3}$ $\frac{2}{3}$

Write the fraction that tells what part of the group is shaded.

c.

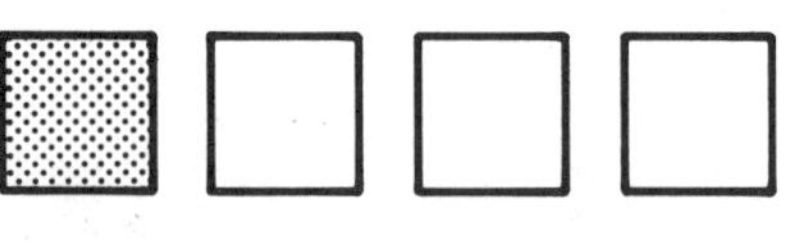
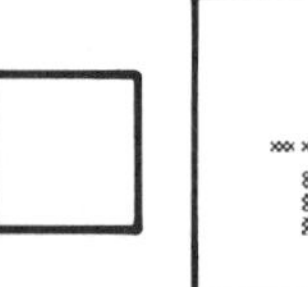

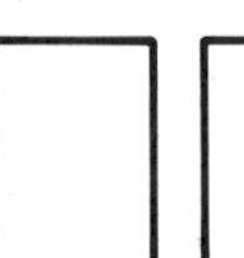
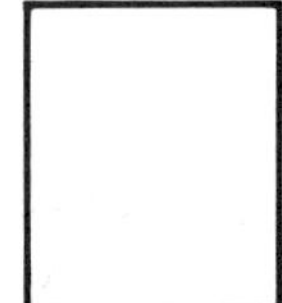

d.

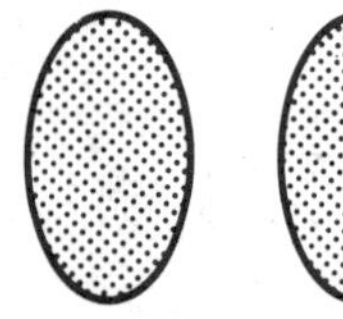
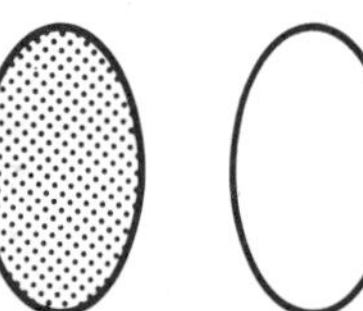
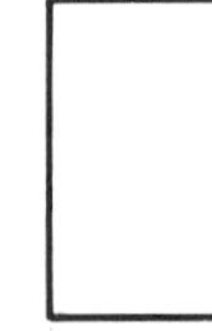
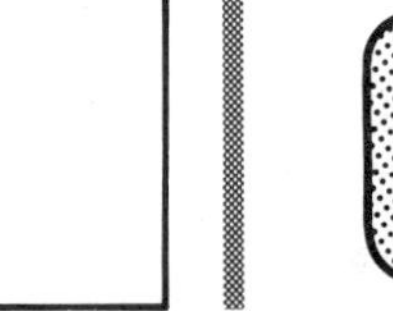

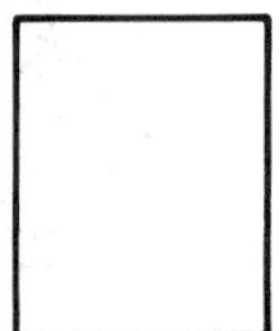

e.

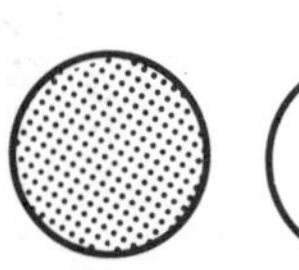
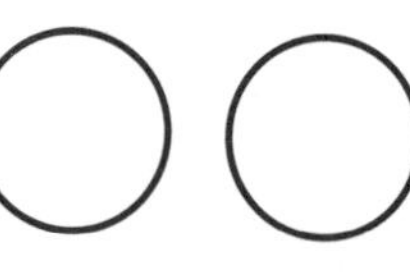

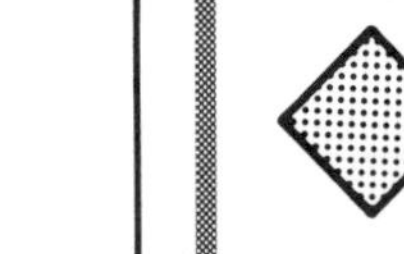

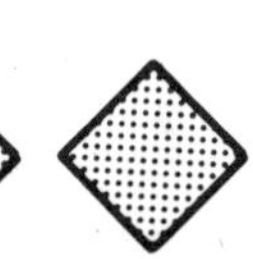
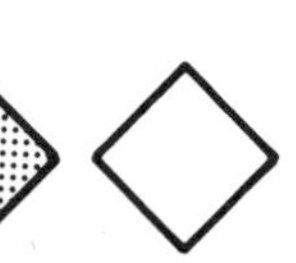
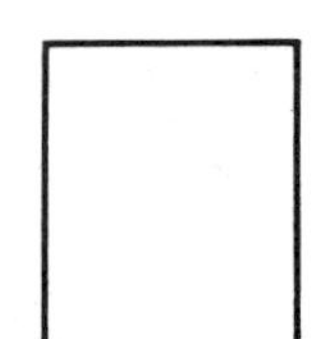

name

PRACTICE

WORKSHEET **90**

Problem Solving • Reading a Table

Name	Warren	Rosita	Karen	Steven	Bonnie	Luis	Su	Tai
Art Projects	8	6	4	2	9	3	7	5

Complete.

a. Who finished more projects?

Karen or Luis

Steven or Tai

b. Who finished fewer projects?

Bonnie or Warren

Rosita or Su

c. Tai finished ______ projects. Bonnie finished ______ projects. How many projects did Tai and Bonnie finish in all? ______

d. Rosita finished ______ projects. Su finished ______ projects. How many projects did Rosita and Su finish in all? ______

e. Luis finished ______ projects. Karen finished ______ projects. Su finished ______ projects. How many projects in all? ______

f. Tai finished ______ projects. Steven finished ______ projects. Bonnie finished ______ projects. How many projects in all? ______

g. How many projects did Rosita, Luis, and Warren finish in all? ______

h. How many projects did Karen, Tai, and Steven finish in all? ______

name

PRACTICE

WORKSHEET **91**

Centimeter

Measure each object to the nearest centimeter.

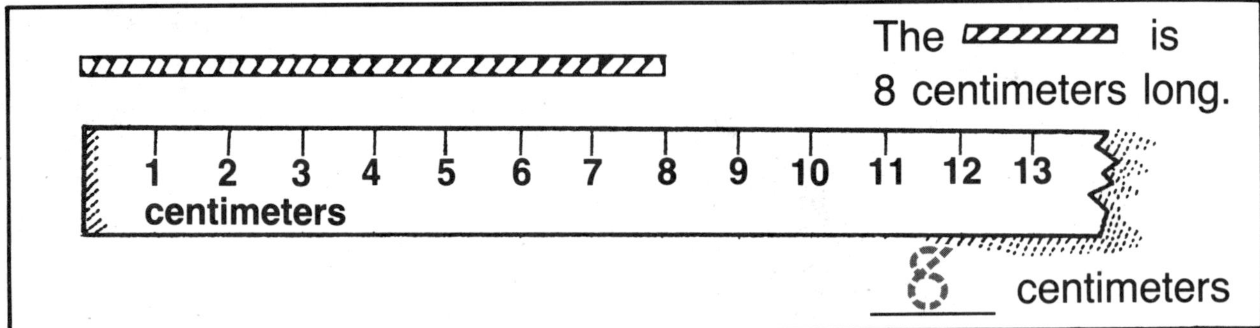

a. 1 2 3 4 5 6 7 8 9 10 11 12 13 centimeters

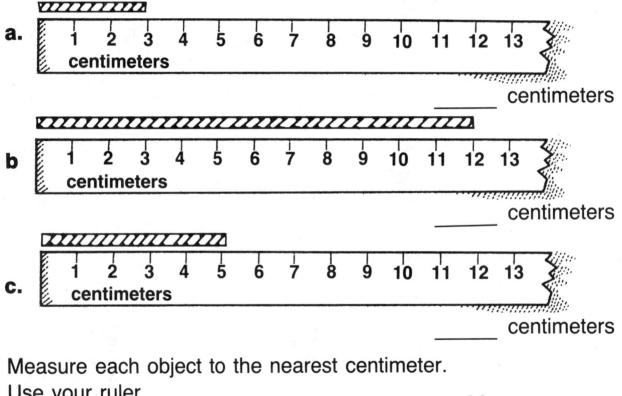

_____ centimeters

b 1 2 3 4 5 6 7 8 9 10 11 12 13 centimeters

_____ centimeters

c. 1 2 3 4 5 6 7 8 9 10 11 12 13 centimeters

_____ centimeters

Measure each object to the nearest centimeter.
Use your ruler.

d. 4 centimeters

e. _____ centimeters

f. _____ centimeters

g. _____ centimeters

name

PRACTICE

WORKSHEET **92**

Perimeter

How far around each figure?

a.

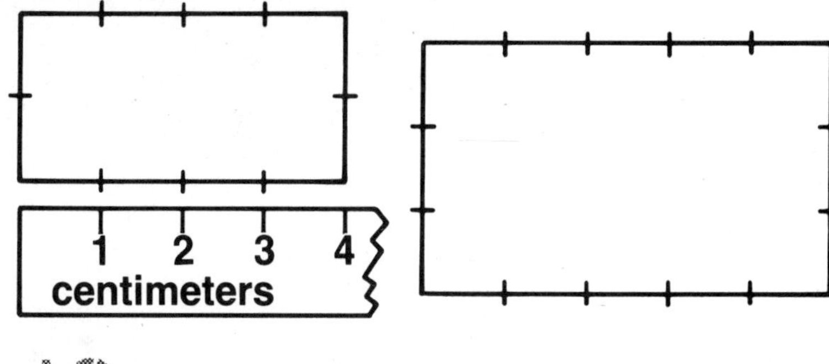

12 centimeters ______ centimeters ______ centimeters

b.

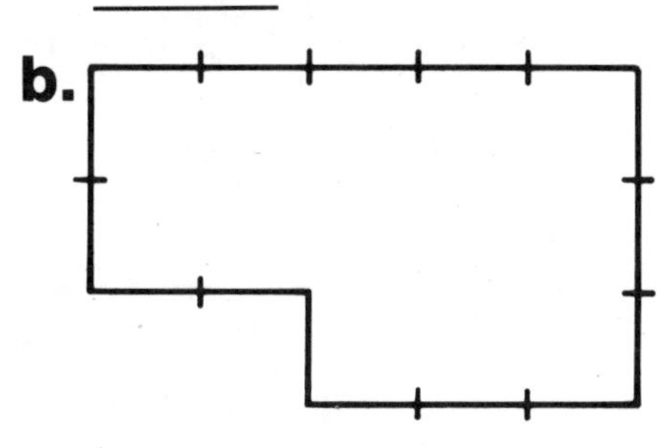

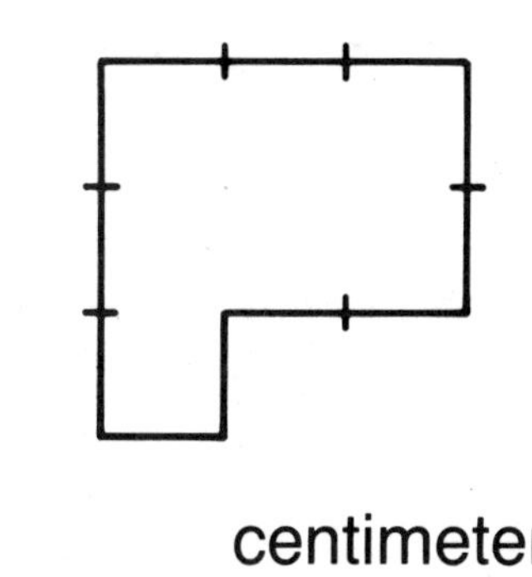

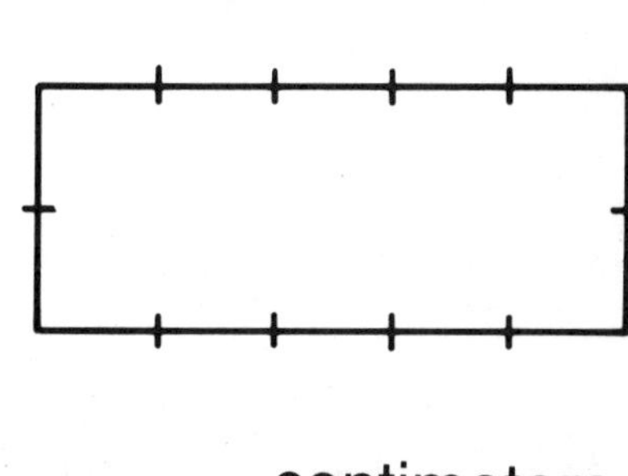

______ centimeters ______ centimeters ______ centimeters

Measure each side.
How far around each figure?

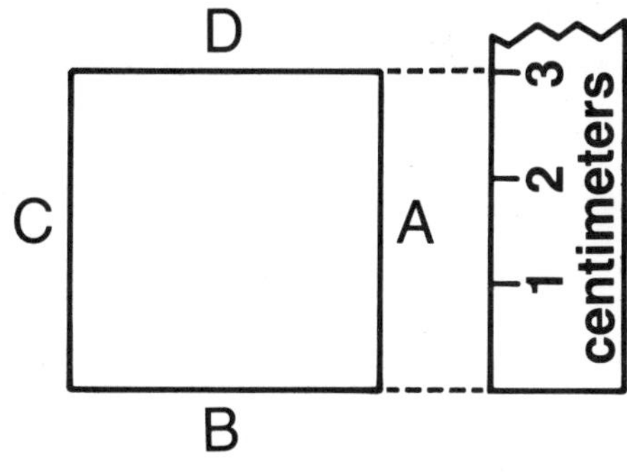

side	centimeters
A	3
B	
C	
D	
sum	

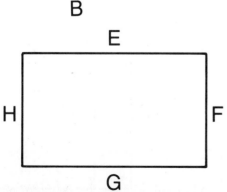

E
H F
G

side	centimeters
E	
F	
G	
H	
sum	

Use with text pages 299–300.

name

PRACTICE

Area

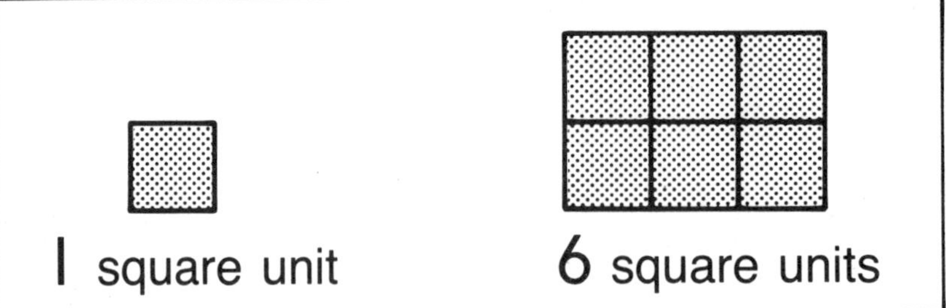

Find how many square units.

a.

8 square units

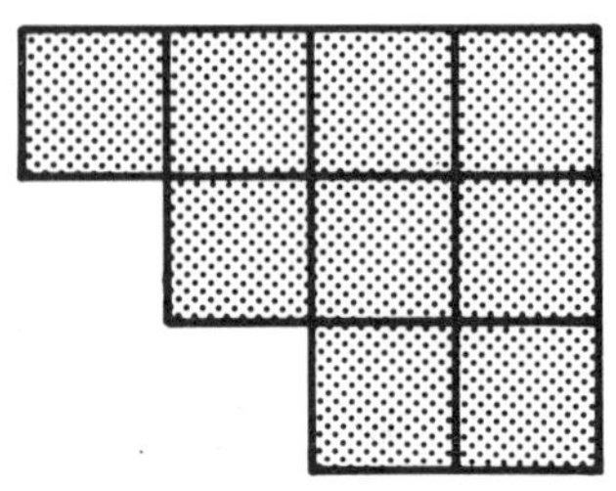

______ square units

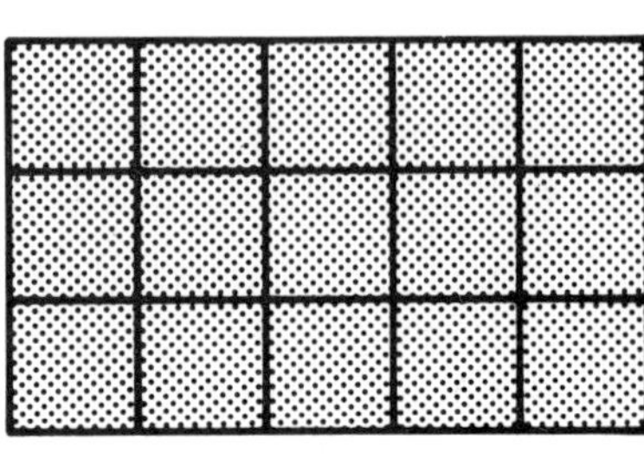

______ square units

b.

______ square units

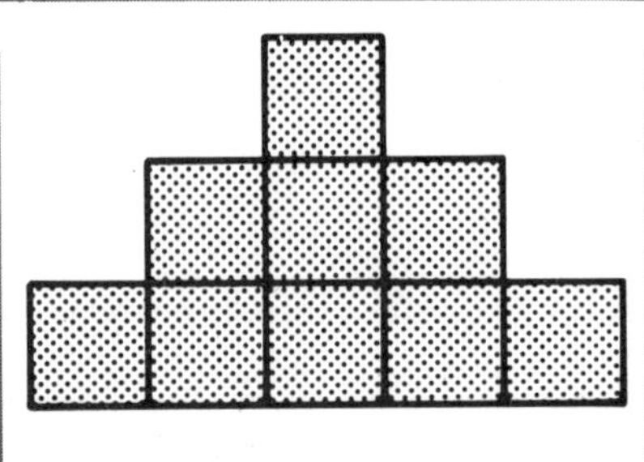

______ square units

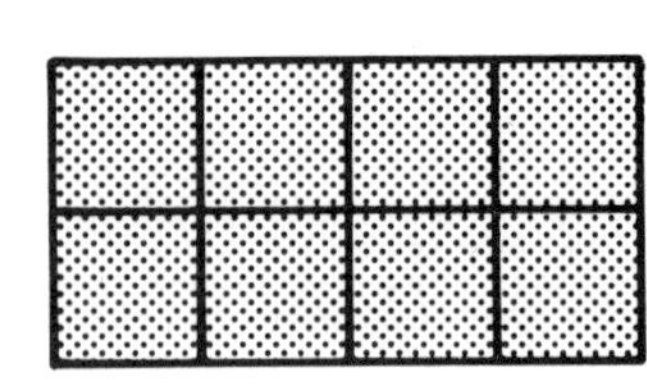

______ square units

Draw the figures.

9 square units

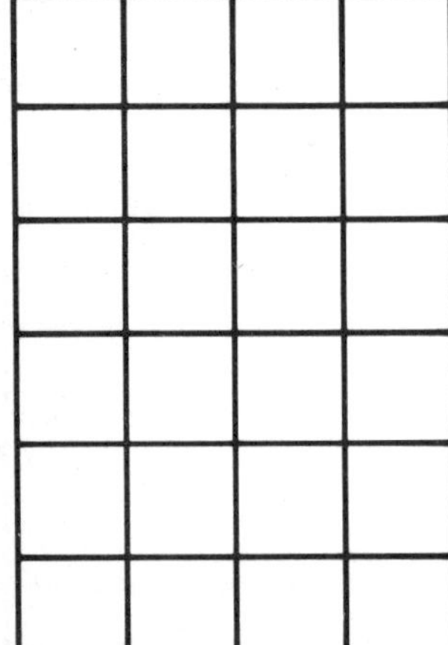

12 square units

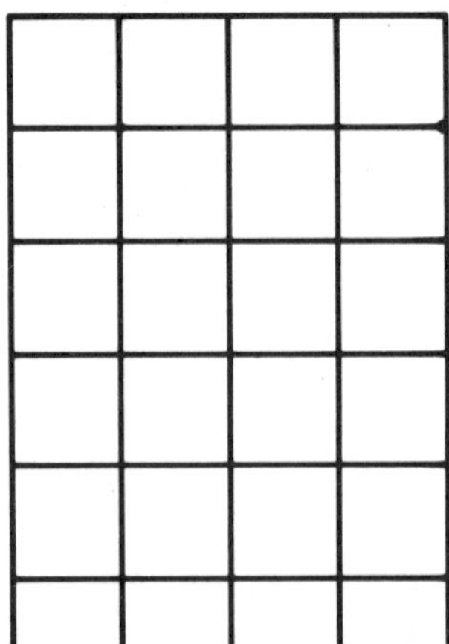

15 square units

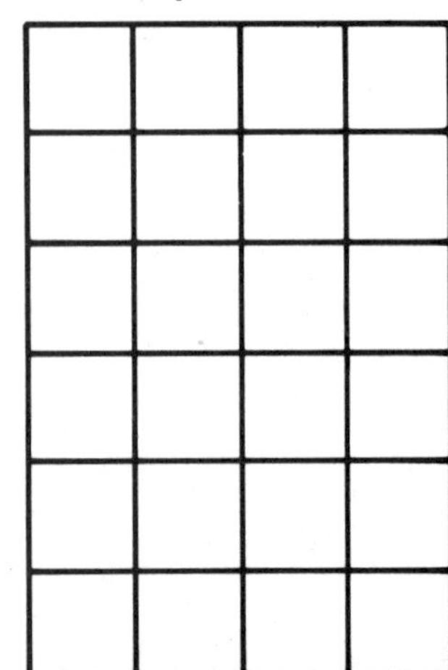

Use with text pages 301–302.

name

PRACTICE

WORKSHEET **94**

Liter

Does the container hold MORE or LESS than one liter?

a.

b. 1 liter MORE LESS

c. 1 liter MORE LESS

d. 1 liter MORE LESS

Problem Solving

Jeffrey made a table to show how many liters some objects can hold.

Object	Liters
kettle	7
can	2
jug	15
jar	1

e. How many liters does the jug hold? ______ liters

f. How many liters does the jar hold? ______ liter

g. How many liters do the kettle and the can hold? ______ liters

h. Which object holds the greatest amount? __________

name

PRACTICE

WORKSHEET **95**

Kilogram

Is the object MORE or LESS than one kilogram?

a.

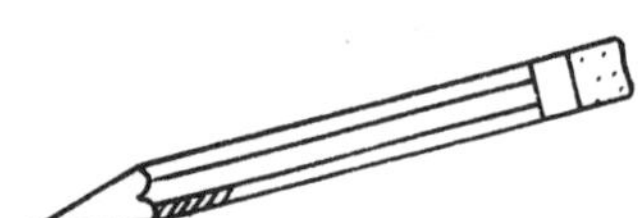

MORE

LESS

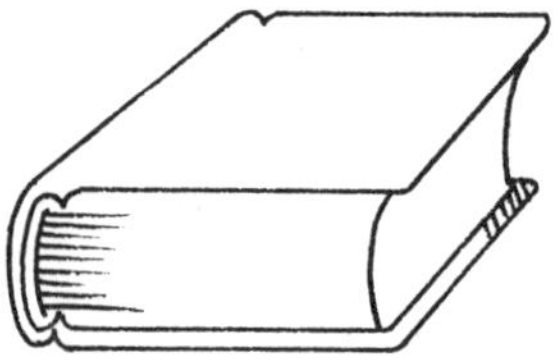

MORE

LESS

b.

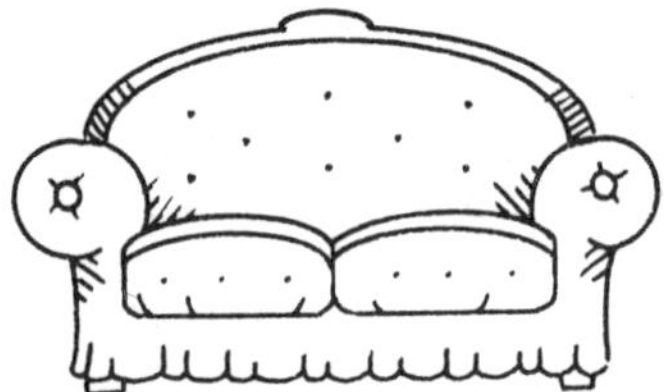

MORE

LESS

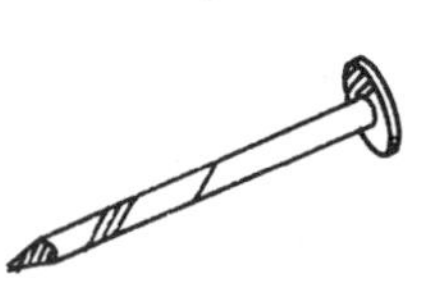

MORE

LESS

What would you use to measure?

c.

centimeter liter kilogram

d.

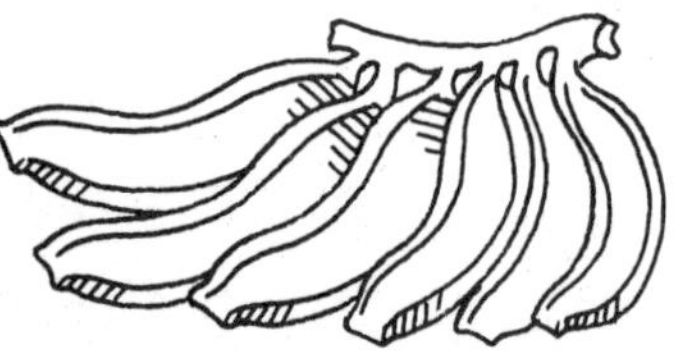

centimeter liter kilogram

e.

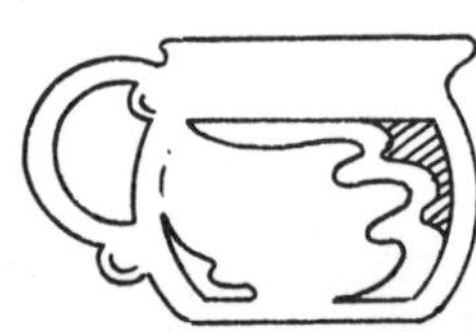

centimeter liter kilogram

name

PRACTICE

WORKSHEET **96**

Temperature

Write the temperature. Use the Celsius thermometer.

a.

40 35 30 25 20 15 10 5 0

0 degrees Celsius ___0___ °C

b.

40 35 30 25 20 15 10 5 0

______ °C

c.

40 35 30 25 20 15 10 5 0

______ °C

d.

______ °C

Write the temperature. Use the Fahrenheit thermometer.

e.

40 35 30 25 20 15 10

30 degrees Fahrenheit ______ °F

f.

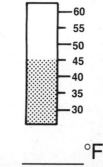

90 85 80 75 70 65 60

______ °F

g.

100 95 90 85 80 75

______ °F

h.

60 55 50 45 40 35 30

______ °F

name

PRACTICE

WORKSHEET **97**

Inch

Measure each object to the nearest inch.

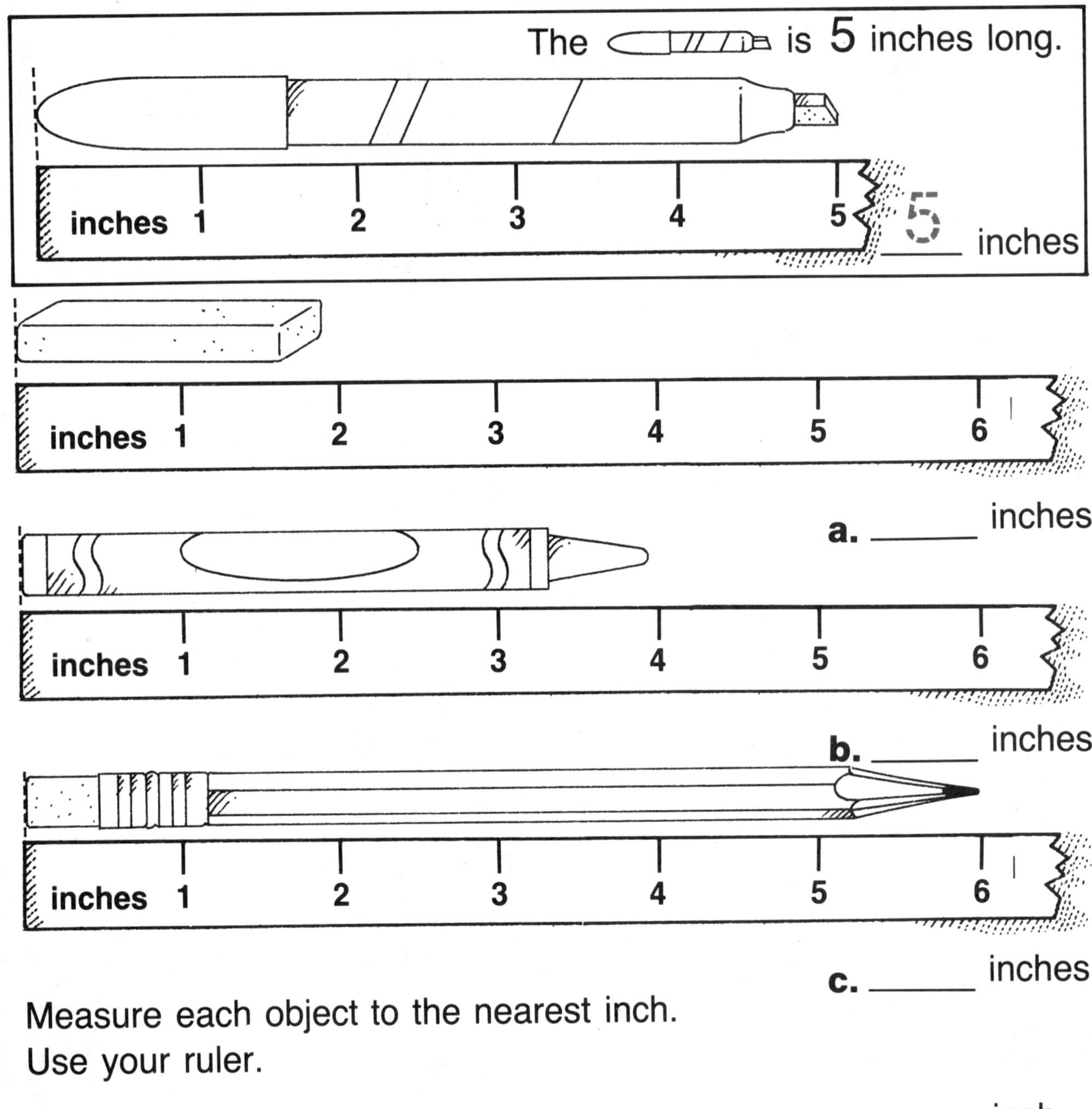

Measure each object to the nearest inch.
Use your ruler.

d. ____ inch

e. ____ inches

f. ____ inches

g. ____ inches

name

PRACTICE

WORKSHEET **98**

Cup, Pint, and Quart

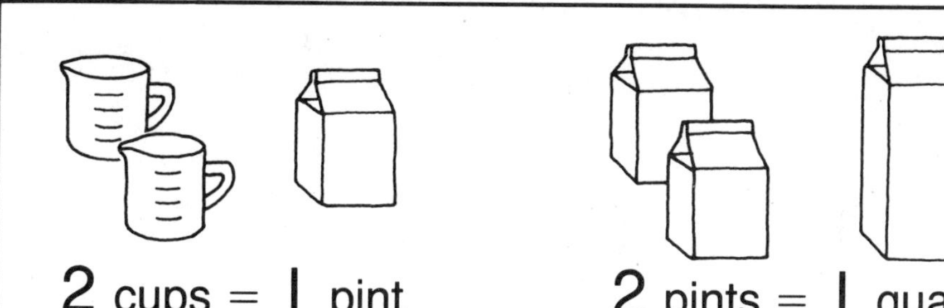

Which holds more?

a.  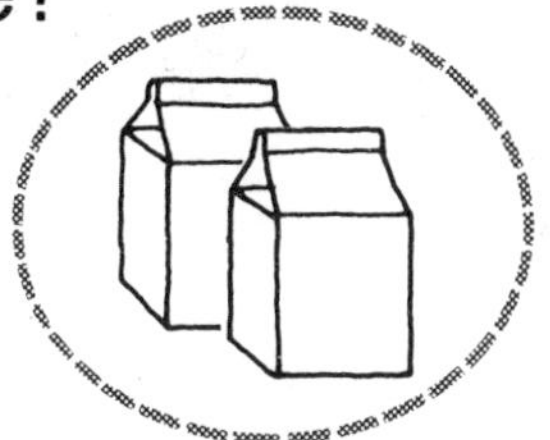  

b.   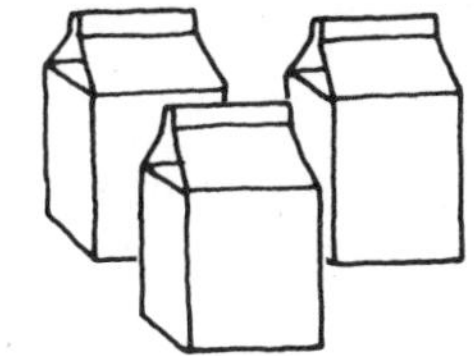 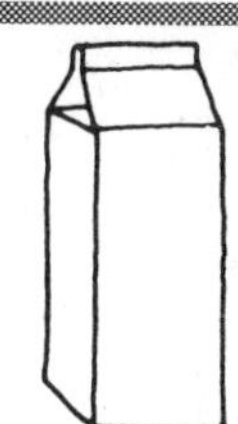

Color to show the same amount.

c.    

d. 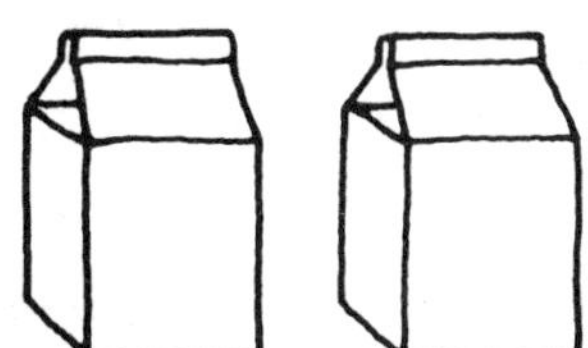 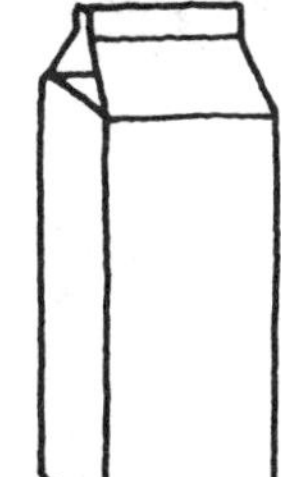 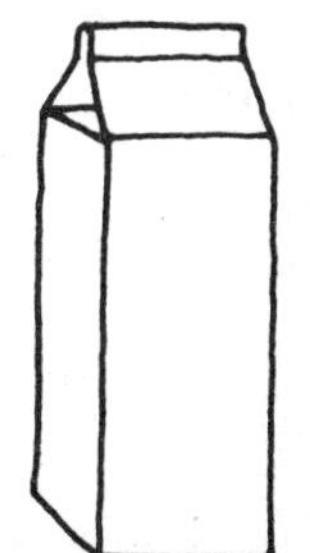

e.      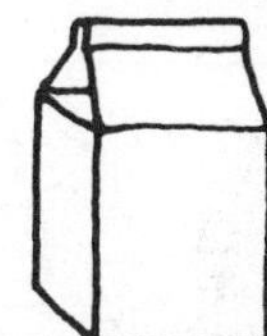

name

PRACTICE

Pound

Use the scale to measure in pounds.

a.

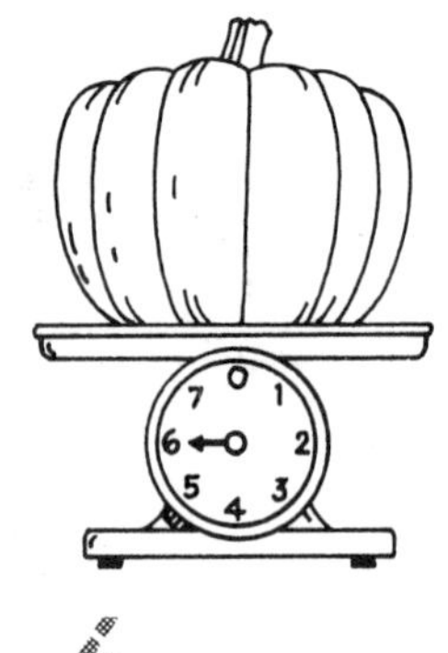

6 pounds

b.

_____ pounds

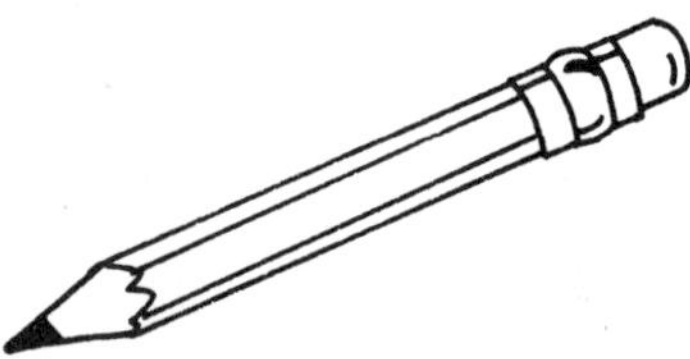

less than 1 pound

1 pound

more than 1 pound

c. Complete the table.

	Less Than 1 Pound	**More Than 1 Pound**
		X

name

PRACTICE

WORKSHEET **100**

Adding Three-Digit Numbers

Step 1
Add the ones.

start ↓ (ones)

hundreds	tens	ones
2	3	6
+4	2	1
		7

Step 2
Add the tens.

hundreds	tens	ones
2	3	6
+4	2	1
	5	7

Step 3
Add the hundreds.

hundreds	tens	ones
2	3	6
+4	2	1
6	5	7

Add.

a.

hundreds	tens	ones
4	5	0
+5	3	6
9	8	6

hundreds	tens	ones
6	2	5
+	5	3

hundreds	tens	ones
3	1	8
+3	7	0

b. 715 + 134 = ____ 614 + 323 = ____ 500 + 100 = ____ 508 + 40 = ____ 415 + 232 = ____

c. 813 + 74 = ____ 225 + 541 = ____ 486 + 312 = ____ 325 + 70 = ____ 724 + 163 = ____

d. 514 + 352 = ________ 235 + 432 = ________

e. 700 + 254 = ________ 116 + 580 = ________

Use with text pages 327–328.

name

PRACTICE

WORKSHEET **101**

Addition with Regrouping

Step 1	Step 2	Step 3
Add the ones. Regroup.	Add the tens.	Add the hundreds.
start ↓ 629 + 154 = 3	1 629 + 154 = 83	1 629 + 154 = 783

Add.

a. 439 + 258 = 697   537 + 23   608 + 347   256 + 316   725 + 159

b. 154 + 29   309 + 525   459 + 329   708 + 58   245 + 318

c. 423 + 135 + 303   526 + 162 + 207   153 + 324 + 215   516 + 133 + 47   302 + 25 + 454

Problem Solving

Solve.

d. The supermarket has 134 cans of vegetables and 209 cans of fruit. How many cans in all?

e. There are 236 bottles of apple juice and 328 bottles of grape juice. How many bottles in all?

Use with text pages 329–330.

name

PRACTICE

WORKSHEET **102 A**

Problem Solving • Using Addition

Add to find the total cost.

a.

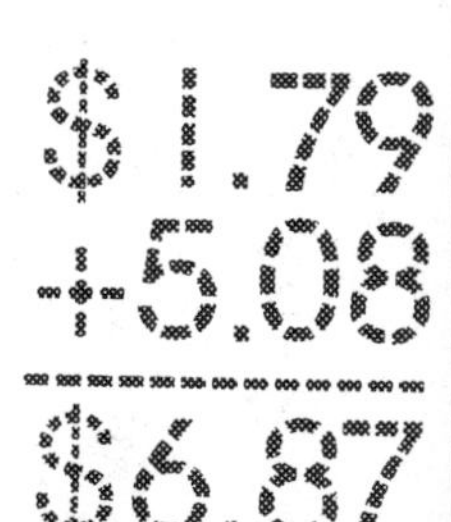

b.

c.

d.

e.

f.

g.

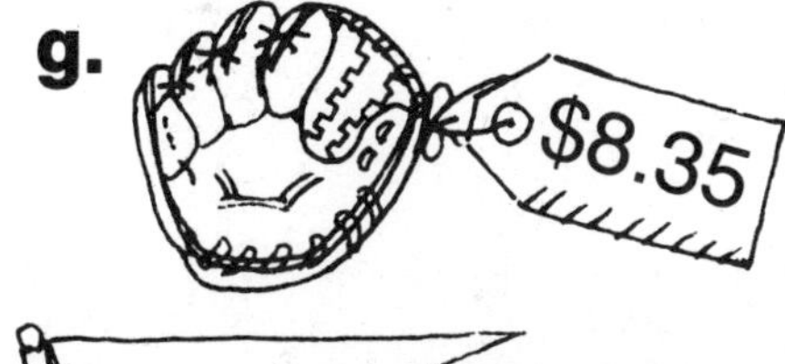

h.

Go on to Worksheet 102B.

name

PRACTICE WORKSHEET **102 B**

Adding Money

Add.

a.	$4.65 + 1.09 = $5.74	$3.67 + 4.27 = $	$5.10 + 4.85	$3.76 + 2.02
b.	$7.36 + 2.47	$5.15 + 3.35	$4.00 + 0.50	$2.07 + 1.45
c.	$7.75 + 1.02	$6.59 + 0.16	$6.45 + 2.00	$8.12 + 0.59
d.	$1.15 + 3.45	$5.16 + 2.40	$1.29 + 6.38	$3.35 + 2.49
e.	$2.15 + 5.62	$3.75 + 2.19	$4.38 + 1.41	$1.59 + 6.25

name

PRACTICE

WORKSHEET **103**

Subtracting Three-Digit Numbers

Step 1

Subtract the ones.

start ↓

hundreds	tens	ones
7	8	4
−5	3	0
		4

Step 2

Subtract the tens.

hundreds	tens	ones
7	8	4
−5	3	0
	5	4

Step 3

Subtract the hundreds.

hundreds	tens	ones
7	8	4
−5	3	0
2	5	4

Subtract.

a.

hundreds	tens	ones
9	6	4
−7	3	4
2	3	0

hundreds	tens	ones
7	8	8
−6	7	3

hundreds	tens	ones
4	5	3
−	4	1

b. $658 - 528$ $739 - 20$ $810 - 600$ $356 - 31$ $875 - 420$

c. $864 - 142$ $974 - 373$ $783 - 50$ $578 - 150$ $968 - 22$

d. 764 − 161 = ______   945 − 405 = ______

e. 875 − 304 = ______   900 − 600 = ______

Use with text pages 335 − 336.

name

PRACTICE

WORKSHEET **104**

Subtraction with Regrouping

Step 1	Step 2	Step 3
You need more ones. Regroup. Subtract the ones.	Subtract the tens.	Subtract the hundreds.
875 − 349 = 6	875 − 349 = 26	875 − 349 = 526

Subtract.

a.	768 − 329 = 439	853 − 405	682 − 17	635 − 107	754 − 625
b.	576 − 69	823 − 518	472 − 56	683 − 244	756 − 137
c.	470 − 244	771 − 67	861 − 524	453 − 36	790 − 357

Problem Solving

Solve.

d. Debbie's reading book has 250 pages. She reads 32 pages. How many pages does she have left to read?

e. Ramón's math book has 352 pages. He finishes 218 pages. How many pages does he have left?

Subtracting Money

Subtract.

a.	$7.32 (2 12) − 2.18 = $5.14	$3.94 − 0.57 = $	$7.48 − 3.07	$7.39 − 2.06
b.	$4.60 − 2.25	$9.72 − 0.54	$7.50 − 2.50	$6.73 − 1.55
c.	$7.36 − 4.08	$5.69 − 0.26	$7.54 − 1.36	$9.50 − 8.02

Subtract to find the new price. BIG SALE

d.

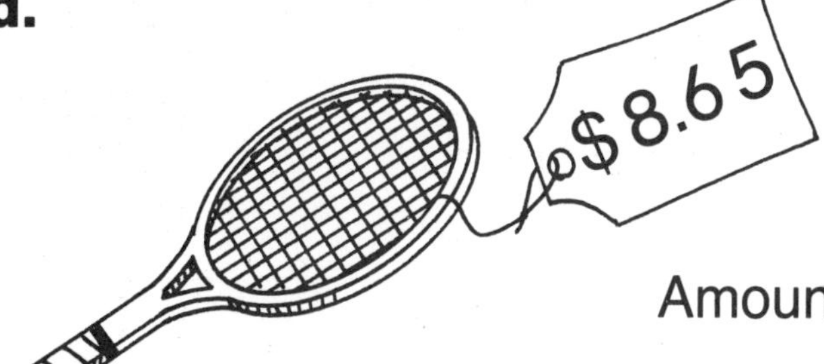

Amount off $1.29

You pay

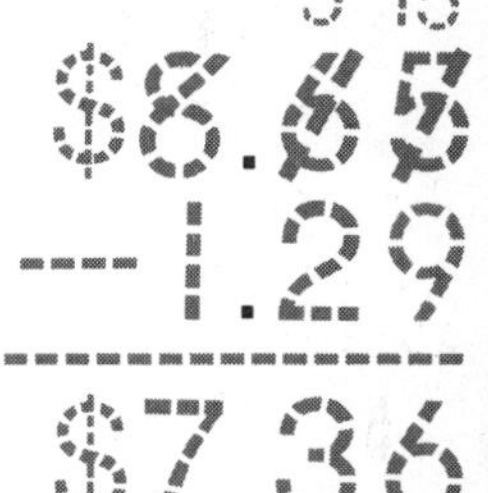

e.

Amount off $3.45

You pay

name

PRACTICE

WORKSHEET **106**

Mixed Practice

Add.	Subtract.
438 +526 964	734 −207 527

Be careful. Watch the signs.

Add or subtract.

a. 458 + 327 = 785   734 − 218   432 − 17   344 + 209

b. 648 − 125   682 + 107   239 + 427   798 − 357

c. 437 + 37   561 − 38   418 + 469   475 − 150

d. \$7.45 − 2.19 = \$.   \$8.60 + 0.25   \$4.39 − 1.00   \$6.34 + 2.05

e. 743 − 215 = ______   174 + 518 = ______

f. 437 + 325 = ______   751 − 314 = ______

Use with text pages 341–342.

name

PRACTICE

Problem Solving • Add or Subtract?

Solve.

a. The post office sells 316 stamps on Monday and 429 stamps on Tuesday. How many stamps are sold in all?

  316
+429
  745

b. The post office receives 484 packages. 146 of these packages are delivered. How many packages are left?

c. The post office gets 837 letters and 205 packages. How many more letters than packages?

d. The post office sells 246 postcard stamps and 307 letter stamps. How many stamps are sold in all?

The post office lists the number of mailboxes in each town.

Town	Number of Mailboxes	Town	Number of Mailboxes
Westville	325	Southland	437
Northtown	126	Eastville	543

How many mailboxes in all?

Which town has more? How many more?

e. Westville and Northtown _____ Eastville or Northtown _____

f. Southland and Eastville _____ Westville or Southland _____

name

PRACTICE

WORKSHEET **108**

2 as a Factor

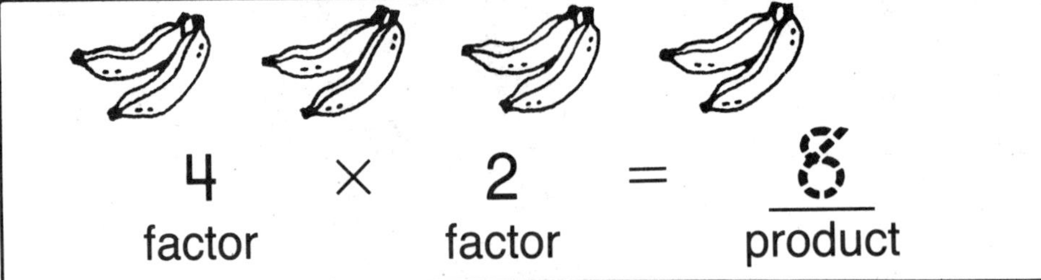

4 × 2 = 8
factor factor product

Multiply.

a.

1 × 2 = 2

5 × 2 = ____

2 × 2 = ____

b. 3 × 2 = ____ 4 × 2 = ____ 1 × 2 = ____

c. 2 × 2 = ____ 3 × 2 = ____ 5 × 2 = ____

d. 1 × 2 = ____ 4 × 2 = ____ 2 × 2 = ____

e. $\begin{array}{r} 2 \\ \times 4 \\ \hline 8 \end{array}$

$\begin{array}{r} 2 \\ \times 1 \\ \hline \end{array}$ $\begin{array}{r} 2 \\ \times 3 \\ \hline \end{array}$ $\begin{array}{r} 2 \\ \times 2 \\ \hline \end{array}$ $\begin{array}{r} 2 \\ \times 5 \\ \hline \end{array}$

f. $\begin{array}{r} 2 \\ \times 2 \\ \hline \end{array}$ $\begin{array}{r} 2 \\ \times 1 \\ \hline \end{array}$ $\begin{array}{r} 2 \\ \times 5 \\ \hline \end{array}$ $\begin{array}{r} 2 \\ \times 4 \\ \hline \end{array}$ $\begin{array}{r} 2 \\ \times 3 \\ \hline \end{array}$ $\begin{array}{r} 2 \\ \times 1 \\ \hline \end{array}$ $\begin{array}{r} 2 \\ \times 4 \\ \hline \end{array}$

g. $\begin{array}{r} 2 \\ \times 5 \\ \hline \end{array}$ $\begin{array}{r} 2 \\ \times 2 \\ \hline \end{array}$ $\begin{array}{r} 2 \\ \times 3 \\ \hline \end{array}$ $\begin{array}{r} 2 \\ \times 1 \\ \hline \end{array}$ $\begin{array}{r} 2 \\ \times 5 \\ \hline \end{array}$ $\begin{array}{r} 2 \\ \times 4 \\ \hline \end{array}$ $\begin{array}{r} 2 \\ \times 3 \\ \hline \end{array}$

name

PRACTICE

WORKSHEET **109**

3 as a Factor

Multiply.

a.

$4 \times 3 =$ 12

$2 \times 3 =$ ____

$5 \times 3 =$ ____

b. $3 \times 3 =$ ____ $5 \times 3 =$ ____ $1 \times 3 =$ ____

c. $2 \times 3 =$ ____ $1 \times 3 =$ ____ $4 \times 3 =$ ____

d. $4 \times 2 =$ ____ $3 \times 3 =$ ____ $3 \times 2 =$ ____

e. $\begin{array}{r} 3 \\ \times 3 \\ \hline 9 \end{array}$

$\begin{array}{r} 3 \\ \times 5 \\ \hline \end{array}$ $\begin{array}{r} 3 \\ \times 1 \\ \hline \end{array}$ $\begin{array}{r} 3 \\ \times 4 \\ \hline \end{array}$ $\begin{array}{r} 2 \\ \times 4 \\ \hline \end{array}$

f. $\begin{array}{r} 3 \\ \times 2 \\ \hline \end{array}$ $\begin{array}{r} 3 \\ \times 1 \\ \hline \end{array}$ $\begin{array}{r} 3 \\ \times 5 \\ \hline \end{array}$ $\begin{array}{r} 2 \\ \times 2 \\ \hline \end{array}$ $\begin{array}{r} 2 \\ \times 1 \\ \hline \end{array}$ $\begin{array}{r} 3 \\ \times 4 \\ \hline \end{array}$ $\begin{array}{r} 2 \\ \times 3 \\ \hline \end{array}$

Problem Solving

Solve.

g. 4 boxes.
3 red in each.
How many red in all?

h. 3 desks.
3 in each.
How many in all?

name

PRACTICE

WORKSHEET **110**

4 as a Factor

Multiply.

a.

$5 \times 4 =$ 20

$1 \times 4 =$ ____

$3 \times 4 =$ ____

b. $2 \times 4 =$ ____ $4 \times 4 =$ ____ $5 \times 4 =$ ____

c. $1 \times 4 =$ ____ $5 \times 3 =$ ____ $2 \times 4 =$ ____

d. $2 \times 2 =$ ____ $3 \times 4 =$ ____ $3 \times 3 =$ ____

e. $\begin{array}{r} 4 \\ \times 2 \\ \hline 8 \end{array}$

$\begin{array}{r} 4 \\ \times 1 \\ \hline \end{array}$ $\begin{array}{r} 4 \\ \times 5 \\ \hline \end{array}$ $\begin{array}{r} 2 \\ \times 3 \\ \hline \end{array}$ $\begin{array}{r} 3 \\ \times 5 \\ \hline \end{array}$

f. $\begin{array}{r} 4 \\ \times 4 \\ \hline \end{array}$ $\begin{array}{r} 3 \\ \times 2 \\ \hline \end{array}$ $\begin{array}{r} 4 \\ \times 3 \\ \hline \end{array}$ $\begin{array}{r} 2 \\ \times 1 \\ \hline \end{array}$ $\begin{array}{r} 4 \\ \times 2 \\ \hline \end{array}$ $\begin{array}{r} 3 \\ \times 3 \\ \hline \end{array}$ $\begin{array}{r} 4 \\ \times 1 \\ \hline \end{array}$

Problem Solving

Solve.

g. 2 boxes.
4 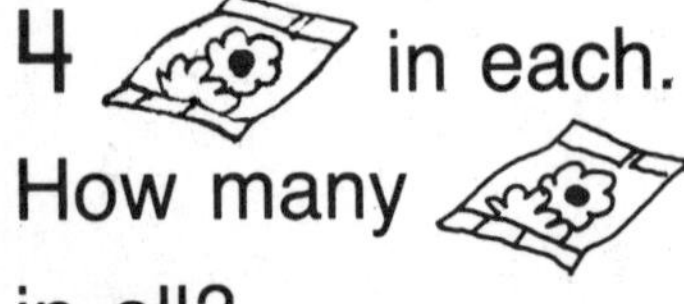 in each.
How many in all?

h. 5 flowerpots.
4  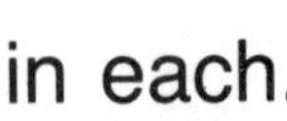 in each.
How many 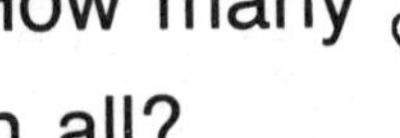
in all?

name

PRACTICE

WORKSHEET 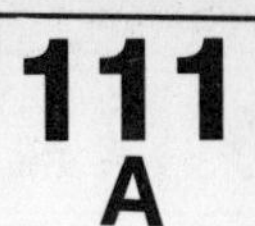

5 as a Factor

Multiply.

a. 

$2 \times 5 =$ 10

$4 \times 5 =$ ____

$1 \times 5 =$ ____

b. $3 \times 5 =$ ____ $5 \times 5 =$ ____ $2 \times 5 =$ ____

c. $3 \times 4 =$ ____ $3 \times 5 =$ ____ $4 \times 5 =$ ____

d. $5 \times 5 =$ ____ $1 \times 4 =$ ____ $3 \times 3 =$ ____

e. $5 \times 3 = 15$ 5×1 5×4 4×2 3×2

f. 5×2 4×4 4×5 3×5 5×5 3×3 5×3

Problem Solving

Solve.

g. 2 bags.
5 in each.
How many in all?

h. 4 boxes.
3 in each.
How many 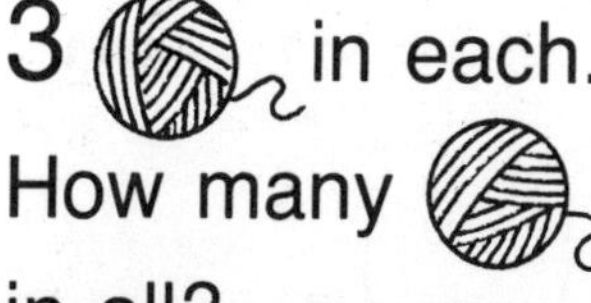 in all?

name

PRACTICE

WORKSHEET 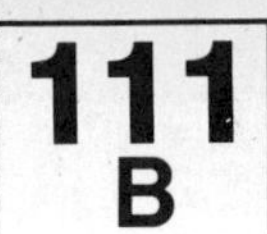

0 and 1 as Factors

The product of any number and 1 is that number.	The product of any number and 0 is 0.
$2 \times 1 = 2$ $\begin{array}{r} 1 \\ \times 3 \\ \hline 3 \end{array}$	$4 \times 0 = 0$ $\begin{array}{r} 0 \\ \times 5 \\ \hline 0 \end{array}$

Find the products.

a. $\begin{array}{r} 0 \\ \times 3 \\ \hline 0 \end{array}$ $\begin{array}{r} 1 \\ \times 4 \\ \hline \end{array}$ $\begin{array}{r} 0 \\ \times 5 \\ \hline \end{array}$ $\begin{array}{r} 1 \\ \times 1 \\ \hline \end{array}$ $\begin{array}{r} 1 \\ \times 3 \\ \hline \end{array}$ $\begin{array}{r} 5 \\ \times 2 \\ \hline \end{array}$ $\begin{array}{r} 4 \\ \times 3 \\ \hline \end{array}$

b. $\begin{array}{r} 0 \\ \times 0 \\ \hline \end{array}$ $\begin{array}{r} 1 \\ \times 5 \\ \hline \end{array}$ $\begin{array}{r} 1 \\ \times 2 \\ \hline \end{array}$ $\begin{array}{r} 0 \\ \times 2 \\ \hline \end{array}$ $\begin{array}{r} 2 \\ \times 2 \\ \hline \end{array}$ $\begin{array}{r} 4 \\ \times 2 \\ \hline \end{array}$ $\begin{array}{r} 3 \\ \times 1 \\ \hline \end{array}$

c. $\begin{array}{r} 4 \\ \times 4 \\ \hline \end{array}$ $\begin{array}{r} 5 \\ \times 3 \\ \hline \end{array}$ $\begin{array}{r} 0 \\ \times 1 \\ \hline \end{array}$ $\begin{array}{r} 5 \\ \times 5 \\ \hline \end{array}$ $\begin{array}{r} 3 \\ \times 2 \\ \hline \end{array}$ $\begin{array}{r} 2 \\ \times 2 \\ \hline \end{array}$ $\begin{array}{r} 4 \\ \times 0 \\ \hline \end{array}$

Multiply the factors in the corners.
Write the products in the circles.

d.

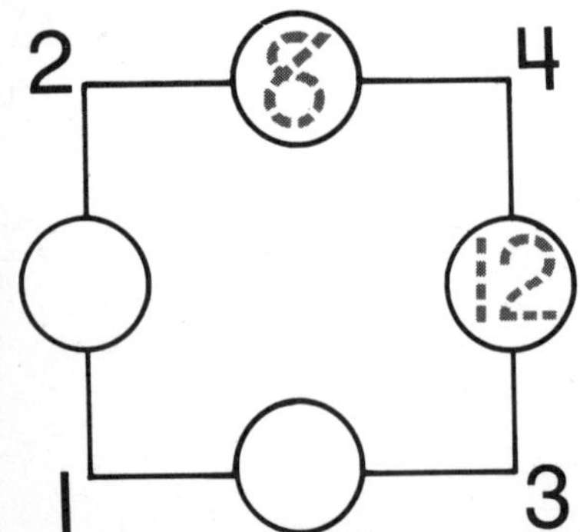

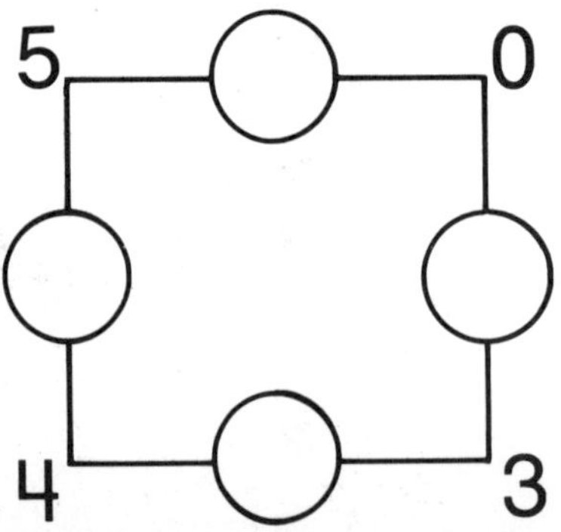

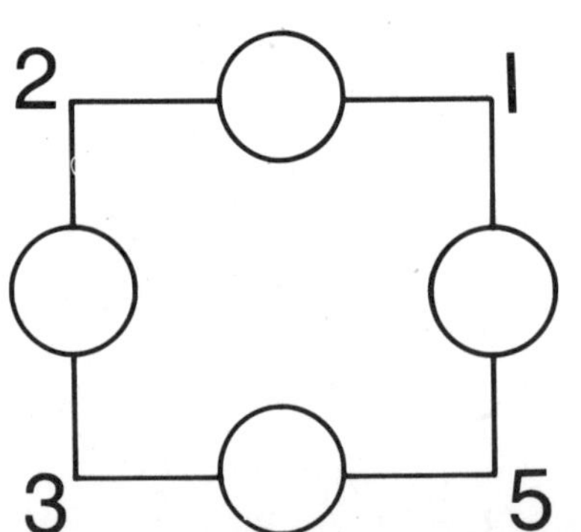

name

PRACTICE

WORKSHEET **112**

Problem Solving • Using Multiplication

Solve.

a.

There are 2 .

Each has 2 .

How many in all?

$$\begin{array}{r} 2 \\ \times 2 \\ \hline 4 \end{array}$$

b.

You have 3 .

3 are in each.

How many in all?

c.

There are 3 .

2 are in each.

How many in all?

d.

There are 5 .

Each has 4 .

How many in all?

Multiply to find the cost.

e.

$$\begin{array}{r} 1¢ \\ \times 2 \\ \hline 2¢ \end{array}$$

Buy 2.

f.

Buy 4.

g.

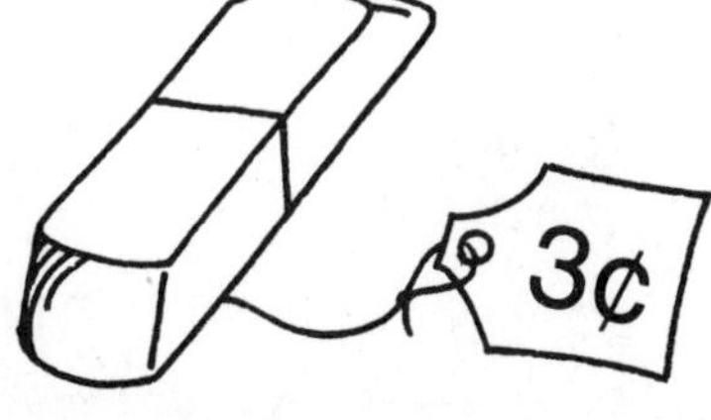

Buy 4.

h.

Buy 4.

name

PRACTICE

WORKSHEET 113 A

Multiplication in Any Order

You can multiply two numbers in either order.
The product is always the same.

$3 \times 5 = 15$

$5 \times 3 = 15$

$$\begin{array}{r} 1 \\ \times 5 \\ \hline 5 \end{array} \qquad \begin{array}{r} 5 \\ \times 1 \\ \hline 5 \end{array}$$

Multiply.

a. $4 \times 5 =$ 20 $\quad 5 \times 2 =$ ____ $\quad 1 \times 3 =$ ____

$5 \times 4 =$ ____ $\quad 2 \times 5 =$ ____ $\quad 3 \times 1 =$ ____

b. $0 \times 4 =$ ____ $\quad 2 \times 3 =$ ____ $\quad 4 \times 3 =$ ____

$4 \times 0 =$ ____ $\quad 3 \times 2 =$ ____ $\quad 3 \times 4 =$ ____

c. $1 \times 4 =$ ____ $\quad 2 \times 0 =$ ____ $\quad 2 \times 4 =$ ____

$4 \times 1 =$ ____ $\quad 0 \times 2 =$ ____ $\quad 4 \times 2 =$ ____

d.
$$\begin{array}{r} 3 \\ \times 2 \\ \hline 6 \end{array} \quad \begin{array}{r} 4 \\ \times 5 \\ \hline \end{array} \quad \begin{array}{r} 0 \\ \times 0 \\ \hline \end{array} \quad \begin{array}{r} 5 \\ \times 3 \\ \hline \end{array} \quad \begin{array}{r} 1 \\ \times 2 \\ \hline \end{array} \quad \begin{array}{r} 5 \\ \times 1 \\ \hline \end{array} \quad \begin{array}{r} 2 \\ \times 5 \\ \hline \end{array}$$

e.
$$\begin{array}{r} 3 \\ \times 1 \\ \hline \end{array} \quad \begin{array}{r} 2 \\ \times 2 \\ \hline \end{array} \quad \begin{array}{r} 3 \\ \times 3 \\ \hline \end{array} \quad \begin{array}{r} 4 \\ \times 2 \\ \hline \end{array} \quad \begin{array}{r} 5 \\ \times 0 \\ \hline \end{array} \quad \begin{array}{r} 1 \\ \times 1 \\ \hline \end{array} \quad \begin{array}{r} 3 \\ \times 4 \\ \hline \end{array}$$

Go on to Worksheet 113B.

name

PRACTICE

WORKSHEET 

Mixed Practice

	Add.	Subtract.	Multiply.
Be careful.	4	4	4
Watch the signs.	+3	−3	×3
	7	1	12

Add, subtract, or multiply.

a.	7	16	5	7	3	12	5
	+6	− 8	×5	+8	×4	− 5	+9
	13						

b.	18	0	15	6	1	2	2
	− 9	×4	− 6	+6	×5	+8	×4

c. $9 + 3 =$ ___ $4 \times 3 =$ ___ $16 - 7 =$ ___

d. $8 + 5 =$ ___ $14 - 9 =$ ___ $4 \times 1 =$ ___

Write +, −, or ×.

e. 2 (+) 6 = 8 12 ◯ 4 = 8 4 ◯ 5 = 20

f. 13 ◯ 7 = 6 2 ◯ 4 = 8 7 ◯ 7 = 1

g. 2 ◯ 3 = 6 6 ◯ 8 = 14 13

Use with text pages 367–368.

name

PRACTICE

WORKSHEET **114**

Problem Solving • Choosing the Operation

Ring the correct example for each question.
Then solve.

a. There are 5 girls and 5 boys at the picnic. How many children in all?

$\begin{array}{r} 5 \\ +5 \\ \hline 10 \end{array}$ (ringed) $\quad \begin{array}{r} 5 \\ \times 5 \\ \hline \end{array}$

b. There are 3 picnic baskets. Each basket holds 5 sandwiches. How many sandwiches in all?

$\begin{array}{r} 5 \\ +3 \\ \hline \end{array} \quad \begin{array}{r} 5 \\ \times 3 \\ \hline \end{array}$

c. There are 14 peaches. There are 6 bananas. How many more peaches than bananas?

$\begin{array}{r} 14 \\ -\ 6 \\ \hline \end{array} \quad \begin{array}{r} 14 \\ +\ 6 \\ \hline \end{array}$

Add, subtract, or multiply to solve.

d. There are 2 teams playing ball. 4 children are on each team. How many children i...

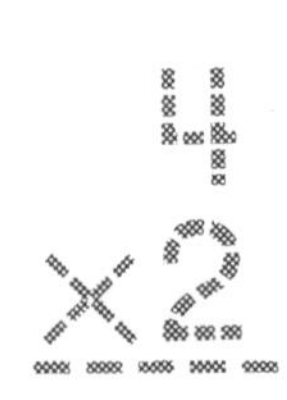

e. There are 15 cans of juice. The children drink 7 cans. How many cans of juice are left?

... 7 blue ... re 9

g. There are 4 piles of paper plates. Each pile has 3 plates. How many paper plates in all?

name

PRACTICE

WORKSHEET 

Division Readiness

 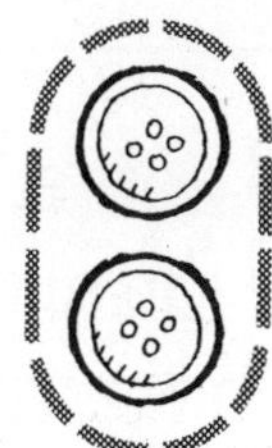 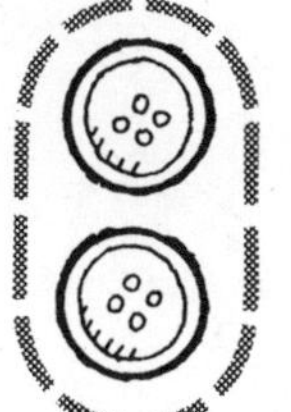 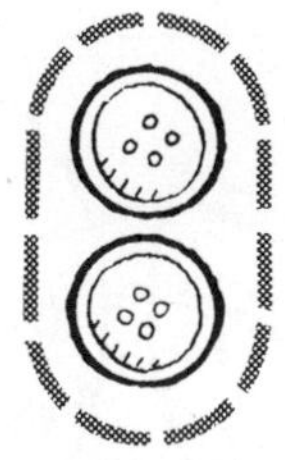

8 buttons.
2 buttons in each group.
There are 4 groups of 2.

Ring groups of 2.

a. 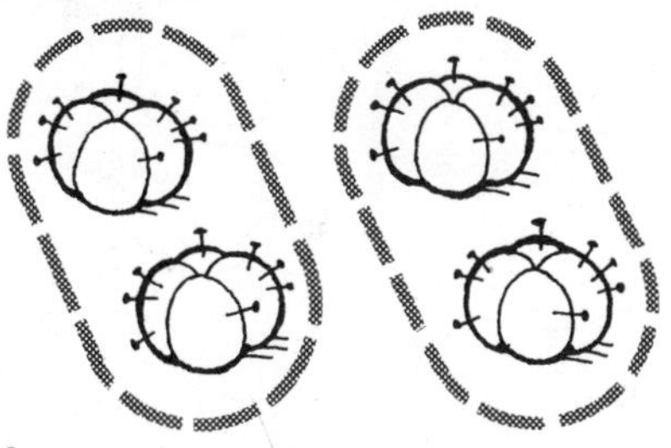

How many groups of 2 are in 4? 

b. 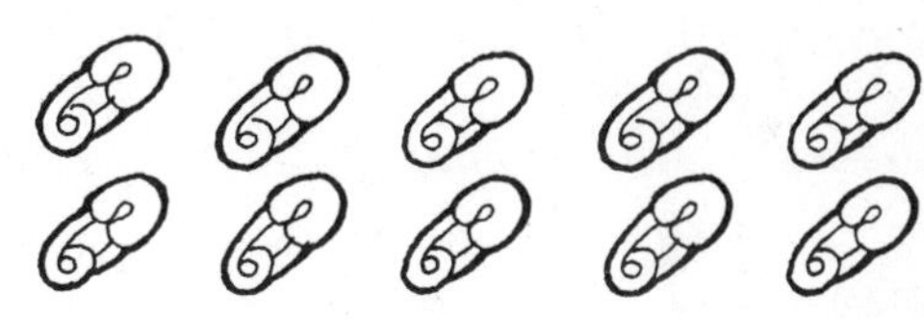

How many groups of of 2 are in 10? ____

Ring groups of 3.

c. 

How many groups of 3 are in 3? ____

d. 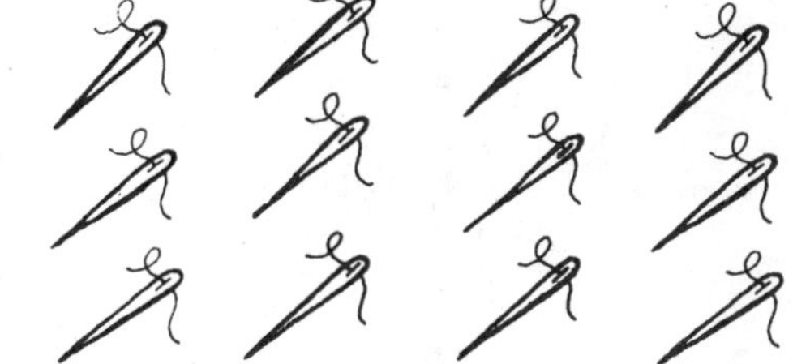

How many groups of 3 are in 12? ____

Ring groups of 4.

e. 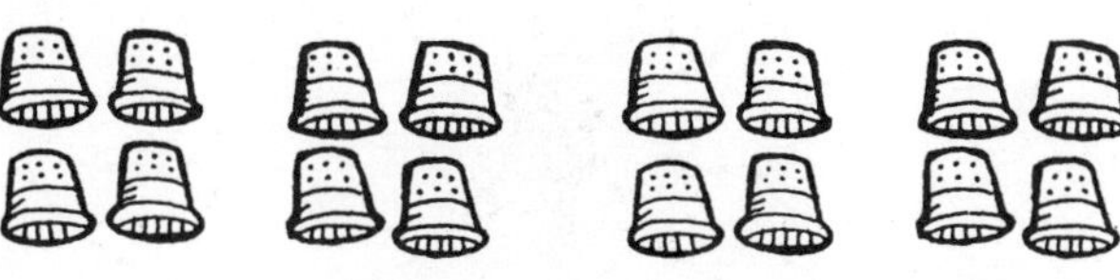

How many groups of 4 are in 16? ____

f. 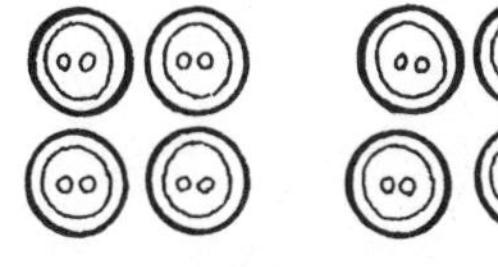      

How many groups of 4 are in 20? ____

Go on to Worksheet 115B.

Use with text pages 371–372.

name ___

PRACTICE WORKSHEET **115 B**

More Division Readiness

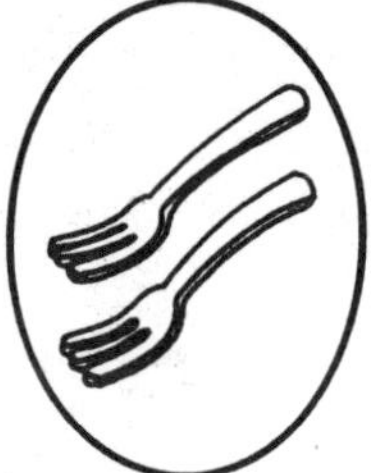

8 forks.
4 groups.
There are 2 forks in each group.

a.

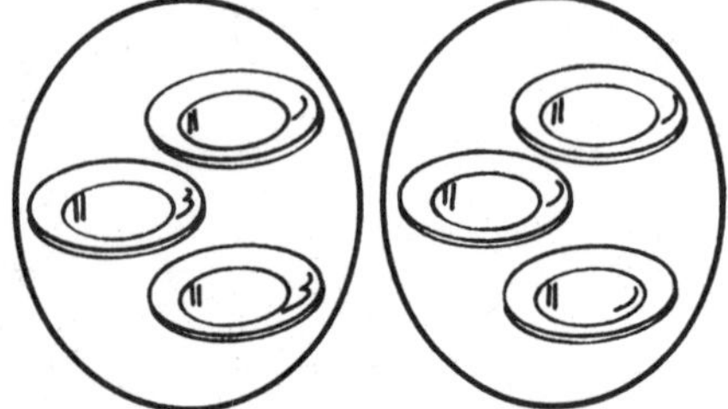

6 plates in 2 equal groups. How many plates in each group?  3

b.

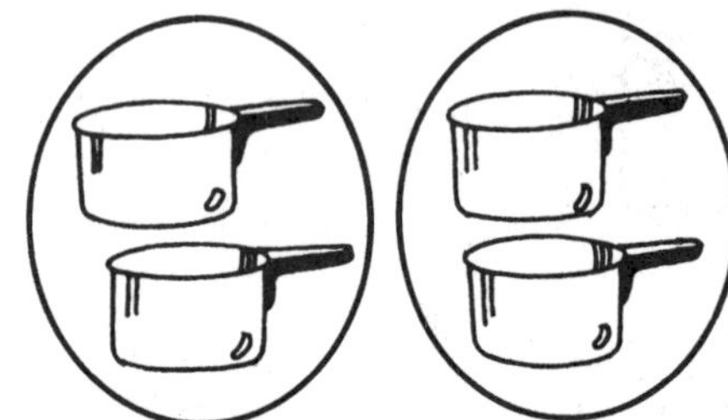

4 pots in 2 equal groups. How many pots in each group? ___

c.

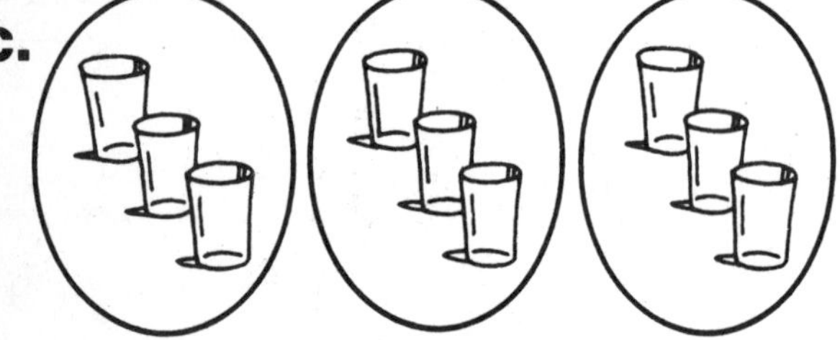

9 glasses in 3 equal groups. How many glasses in each group? ___

d.

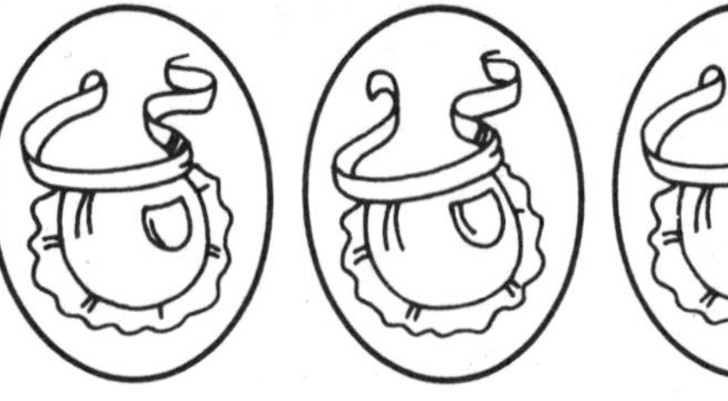

3 aprons in 3 equal groups. How many aprons in each group? ___

e.

10 cups in 5 equal groups. How many cups in each group? ___

f.

8 pans in 2 equal groups. How many pans in each group? ___